CRYSTAL BROOKS

Scientific Calculator Sourcebook

A collection of facts, examples, information, and techniques illustrating how you can use your *Advanced Professional Calculator* as a powerful decision-making tool in business, scientific and everyday life situations.

Note: The calculator keystrokes and descriptions in this book are based on the TI-54.

This book was developed by:

The Staff of the Texas Instruments Learning Center

Kathy A. Kelly
Robert E. Whitsitt, II
M. Dean LaMont
Dr. Ralph A. Oliva, Educational Software Director

And:

The Staff of the University of Denver Mathematics Laboratory
Dr. Ruth I. Hoffman, Director
Michael Zastrocky
James F. Reed
Dr. Sam Battaglia

With contributions by:

Mahendra P. Agrawal
Samir W. Rizk
Lane L. Douglas
Charles L. McCollum
Harry Alderman
Dr. Paul Staiert
Dr. George Bardwell
Ross Wise
Joe Poyner

Artwork and layout were coordinated and executed by:

Gaither and Davy Design Inc.

And:

Deason and Schenck Associates

IMPORTANT

Texas Instruments makes no warranty, either express or implied, including but not limited to any implied warranties of merchantability and fitness for a particular purpose, regarding these book materials and makes such materials available solely on an "as-is" basis.

In no event shall Texas Instruments be liable to anyone for special, collateral, incidental, or consequential damages in connection with or arising out of the purchase or use of these materials and the sole and exclusive liability to Texas Instruments, regardless of the form of action, shall not exceed the purchase price of this book.

TABLE OF CONTENTS Σ+

TABLE OF CONTENTS

xꞓy

Introduction

Hand-held calculators, such as the TI-54, have made mathematics easier. A new speed, confidence, and accuracy are now possible in handling the arithmetic parts of our lives. As hand-held calculators continue in their rapid evolution, advanced professional machines handling increasingly complicated mathematics are available. Many techniques that previously required large volumes of tables, tedious calculations, or access to a large computer center can now be carried out with a few keystrokes on a hand-held calculator.

This book discusses how the TI-54 makes it easy for you to use the powerful statistical, mathematical, and scientific functions, concentrating on how to use these functions, stating them in a straightforward manner with examples and keystroke solutions. For those who want to know more about the details and theory, there is a brief survey of some of the basics of statistics.

The Story of Statistics

The science of statistics (as now known) traces its history to a gambler. In 1654 Antoine Gombaud, a young nobleman from France with the title of Chevalier de Méré, was concerned over his luck at the gaming tables. He sought advice and counsel from the noted French mathematician, Blaise Pascal. Among the problems he put to Pascal was the question of how prize money should be divided among the players if a game is interrupted for some reason.

This question led Pascal into the study of probabilities. Particularly he evaluated the probability of one given player winning if a cancelled game were continued to completion. Pascal wrote a letter about these problems and his work on games of chance to another famous French mathematician, Pierre de Fermat. The resulting exchange of letters was the beginning of the evolving science of statistics.

The Story of Calculators

Blaise Pascal was an interesting and productive man. While working with the science of probability and statistics, he also was working with what became one of the world's first "calculating machines" using the ideas of men such as John Napier. Pascal's work in this area began the evolution of the mechanical calculator. The first machines handled calculations rather slowly with the aid of complex entanglements of whirling gears, whizzing cranks, wheels, and windows. This evolution continued on up through 1890, when the punched card helped to take the 1890 U.S. Census. This led the way to later electric relay devices which continued to evolve into large-scale computers.

A few years ago, people working in the electronics industry made several breakthroughs that resulted in the integrated circuit (IC). Integrated circuits made it possible to process and store large amounts of information in very small spaces with little power and at low cost. These devices, coupled with the development of the inexpensive "Liquid Crystal Display" (LCD) made hand-held calculators a reality. Recent advances in integrated circuits are continuing to increase the amount of information storage and processing that can be handled on a single "IC chip". (The term "IC chip" refers to the tiny piece of silicon upon which an integrated circuit is fabricated.)

New highly flexible IC chips are making today's advanced professional and programmable hand-held calculators possible. With these advanced machines, highly complex mathematical calculations can be executed rapidly and accurately with the touch of a key.

The "Scientific Calculator Sourcebook"

Mathematics is part of many everyday, scientific, and business activities. Your calculator can quickly and accurately handle the mathematics side of life. Also, your advanced professional calculator can be a powerful ally as you make decisions. This book has been designed to show you how.

This book gives compact, accessible, step-by-step techniques enabling you to take a variety of decision-making situations and analyze them with keyboard solutions. The book was designed to work directly with the calculator, so be sure to use them together.

An important first step is to get thoroughly acquainted with your calculator, Chapter 1 of this book is a quick explanation of all the features and keys of the calculator, along with brief examples illustrating the use of each feature. Chapter 1 is divided into six major sections:

Section 1 — Keyboard and Display Basics
Section 2 — Data Entry and Clearing Keys
Section 3 — Mathematical Functions
Section 4 — Conversion Keys
Section 5 — Complex Number Keys
Section 6 — Statistical Keys

The subsequent chapters in the book give examples that illustrate how you can work with your machine. In each case a real life, business, mathematics, or science situation is analyzed for you.

THE "SCIENTIFIC CALCULATOR SOURCEBOOK"

Each example is broken down into the following segments; each identified with its own graphic symbol, as shown:

Target: A brief statement of what types of calculation are used to analyze the problem, and how to begin implementing the calculation.

Tools: The formulas and facts needed to solve the problem along with a brief statement as to why each is used, where the techniques come from, and how they are tailored to the specific example.

Keying it in: Sample keystrokes to execute the solution (using the data given in the example), along with what you'll see in the display at key points in the calculation.

Decision Time: How to use the results of the calculation in arriving at a conclusion or decision.

Going Further: For some examples, a "going further" section is included. It discusses how additional information or conclusions may be drawn from the calculation just completed.

While you're busy using your calculator, don't forget that even though it has the latest in solid-state technology, it still qualifies as a great toy for children of all ages. Play with it! Use it for exploring and "what iffing," as well as just idle doodling on the keys. You may just find yourself exploring patterns and relationships which can lead you to a new appreciation of the beautiful side of numbers and mathematics.

The Keys

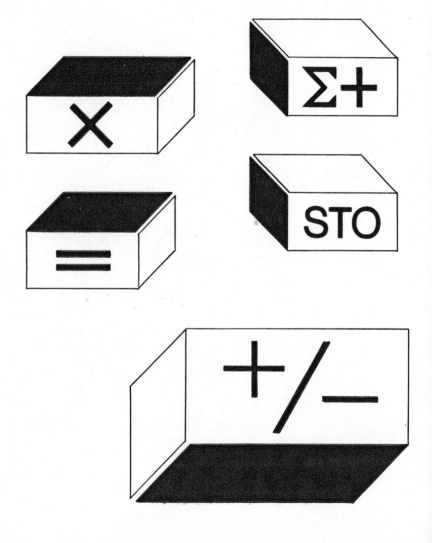

Introduction

The integrated circuit, which made handheld calculators possible, appeared only a few years ago. Texas Instruments invented the integrated circuit, the microprocessor, and the microcomputer which have made TI synonymous with reliability, affordability and compactness. The TI-54 calculator has many capabilities that make it an excellent choice for scientific applications. Its features include:

● AOS™ Algebraic Operating System

Comprehensive data entry with the number and decimal keys, a π key, a key to exchange x and y values, and parentheses. The Algebraic Operating System allows the entry of most problems as they are written with up to four operations and 15 parentheses pending. Seven user data memories with memory arithmetic are available. Data may be entered and displayed in standard format (with the necessary number of decimal places), in scientific format, or in engineering format.

● Mathematical and Scientific Functions

Mathematical and scientific keys for all frequent needs, including reciprocal, square, square root, universal powers and roots, percent, percent change, constant, absolute value, integer part, fractional part, factorial, permutations, combinations, logarithms and antilogarithms, in both common and natural form, and all common trigonometric and hyperbolic functions and their inverses.

● Complex Numbers

Complex numbers may be entered in either rectangular or polar form. The functions square, square root, reciprocal, logarithms and antilogarithms in both common and natural form, and absolute value operate immediately on the complex number with results in rectangular form. Chain arithmetic is used with the following functions: universal powers and roots, multiplication, division, addition, and subtraction with results displayed in rectangular form.

● Built-in Conversions

Angular measures are displayed in degrees, radians, or grads, and easily convertible from one to the other. Conversion keys for polar coordinates to rectangular coordinates, degrees/minutes/seconds to decimal degrees, and the reverse of both of these, in complex and other modes.

● Statistical Functions

A full range of statistical keys, including simple data entry and correction with multiple data point capability, mean, and both population and sample standard deviation. Also available are keys used in calculating linear regression and trend line problems, including correlation, slope, intercept, and one value given another.

With the TI-54, you can solve problems and get information that previously would have required a large computer. By understanding all of the features and becoming completely acquainted with what your calculator can (and cannot) do, you can solve problems and get information quickly and easily. This book is designed to explain, with many examples, what the TI-54 calculator can do.

This chapter explains the essential features and keys of the calculator. Included is some information on why each key is important as well as how each is used.

The Sections of the chapter are listed below. If you are familiar with the basics of the calculator, you may want to go immediately to the application chapters.

Section 1—Keyboard and Display Basics
Section 2—Data Entry and Clearing Keys
Section 3—Mathematical Functions
Section 4—Conversion Keys
Section 5—Complex Number Keys
Section 6—Statistical Keys

Section 1—Keyboard And Display Basics

This Section is a quick explanation of the basics. Please keep the calculator with you so you can see the use of each feature as it is presented.

Turn the calculator on with the [ON/C] key (at the top right of the keyboard). A zero appears in the display and a number of indicators may appear. To initially ready the calculator for normal calculations, press the key marked [2nd] (at the top left of the keyboard) and then the key marked [=] with **CSR** above it (at the lower right of the keyboard). Press the key marked [INV] (on the left side four rows from the top) and then the key marked [Img] (the second from the left on the top row). Press the key marked [2nd] (at the top left of the keyboard), and the key marked [K] with **CM** above it (near the top left of the keyboard). The display now shows a zero. This sequence should always be performed after replacing the batteries.

THE KEYBOARD

The calculator has many features that make calculations easy and accurate. To allow the use of all these features without crowding the keyboard, many of the keys have more than one function. Notice that many of the keys have symbols printed above them in addition to those on them. The symbols printed above the keys are second functions. To perform one of these functions, press the [2nd] key and then press the key for the function that you wish to perform. Pressing the [2nd] key twice, returns the following key to its first function.

In this book, key symbols for first functions are shown with black print on a white background. Key symbols with a black background are used to indicate second functions.

The keys in the third, fourth, and fifth rows are grouped together by vertical stripes. These keys and their second functions have an inverse function. To perform the inverse functions of these keys, press the [INV] key and then the key for the function. For example, pressing [INV] [sin] finds the arcsine (sin⁻¹) of the number in the display. Pressing [INV] twice returns the following key to its non-inverse function. The keys [INV] and [2nd] may be used in any order in normal calculations.

THE DISPLAY

CMPLX   RAD

Turn the calculator on with the [ON/c] key. The [ON/c] key is also used to clear entries and operations and the word "Error" from the display. The display shows "Error" when overflow or underflow occurs or when an improper operation is requested. See the Error Conditions section in the Appendix for more information.

The word CALC appears in the display any time the calculator is performing calculations. This occurs briefly except when doing certain statistical problems or solving problems involving complex numbers. No keyboard entries are accepted while CALC is in the display.

Turning the calculator off (with the [OFF] key) and back on (with the [ON/c] key) removes the number in the display and pending calculations. Other numbers, in user data memories or statistical registers, as well as the mode the calculator is in (statistics or complex number) stay in the machine. The calculator always comes on in the degree mode.

Statistics Mode Indicator

If STAT is displayed, the calculator is in the statistics mode. Because of the Constant Memory™ feature, the calculator retains the mode it was in when it was turned off. The statistics mode is set when [Σ+] or [2nd] [Frq] is pressed. If the calculator is in the complex number mode, the statistics mode can only be selected by first returning to the normal calculation mode. [2nd] [CSR] clears the statistical registers, STAT indicator, and returns the calculator to the normal calculation mode. The STAT mode is also cleared if there is an error due to the data when determining the mean, correlation, slope, intercept, or standard deviation. See the *Statistical Keys Section* for more information.

SECTION 1—KEYBOARD AND DISPLAY BASICS

Complex Number Mode Indicators

If CMPLX is displayed, the calculator is in the complex number mode. The complex number mode is set when [Img] or [θ] is pressed. If the calculator is in the statistics mode, the complex number mode can only be selected by first returning to the normal calculation mode. Pressing [INV] [Img] or [INV] [θ] clears the CMPLX indicator, pending operations, imaginary part in memory, and returns the calculator to the normal calculation mode. Additionally, when [θ] is pressed, r, θ is displayed indicating that the number in the display is in polar form. Thus when complex numbers are in polar form, both the CMPLX and r, θ indicators are displayed. See the *Complex Number Keys Section* for more information.

Angular Mode Indicators

RAD indicates radian mode, and GRAD indicates grad mode. If neither RAD or GRAD is in the display, the calculator is in the degree mode. The angular units may be changed with the [DRG], [INV] [DRG], [2nd] [DRG▸], and [INV] [2nd] [DRG▸] keys. The calculator always returns to the degree mode when it is turned off and back on. See the *Conversion Keys Section* for more information.

APD™ AUTOMATIC POWER DOWN

To conserve power, after 15 to 35 minutes of nonuse the calculator is automatically powered down through the APD™ feature. However, just turning it back on allows you to continue in the state the calculator was in, and use the values in the user data memories. Any pending operations and intermediate values are lost. The effect is the same as if you had pressed the [OFF] key.

Section 2—Data Entry And Clearing Keys

The following keys are used in entering and manipulating data to be used in subsequent calculations.

[0] - [9]—DIGIT KEYS

The digit keys allow any number to be entered into the display in a logical left-to-right order.

[π]—PI KEY

The [π] key enters the value of pi to 11 significant digits, with a value of 3.1415926536. The display shows the value of pi rounded to eight digits, or 3.1415927.

[•]—DECIMAL POINT KEY

The calculator operates with a floating decimal point which can be placed wherever needed. The decimal point is not displayed for integer numbers. A zero precedes the decimal point for numbers less than one. Zeros trailing the last significant digit on the right of a decimal point are not displayed unless the [2nd] [Fix] key has been used to fix the number of decimal places displayed.

[+/−]—CHANGE SIGN KEY

Pressing the change sign key instructs the calculator to change the sign of the displayed value. This allows the use of negative numbers in calculations.

[x⇄y]—X EXCHANGE Y KEY

In some calculating situations, the roles of x and y may be reversed after they have been entered. This key can be used to reverse the factors in subtraction, the divisor and dividend in division, or x and y in Δ%, y^x, and $\sqrt[x]{y}$. It is also used in statistical calculations and polar to rectangular conversions in the normal calculation mode as discussed later.

[ON/c], [2nd] [CM], [2nd] [CSR]—CLEARING KEYS

The [ON/c] key is used to clear entries and operations. If an error is made when entering a number, press the [ON/c] key once and reenter the number. *If an operation key has already been pressed, pressing the [ON/c] key clears all pending operations and the operands entered. Pressing the [ON/c] key twice always clears the display and all pending operations and operands from the calculator.* The user data memories and statistical registers are not affected by this key.

SECTION 2—DATA ENTRY AND CLEARING KEYS

The [2nd] [CM] key clears the values from the user data memories. It does not affect data in the statistical registers.

The [2nd] [CSR] key clears the statistical registers and the STAT indicator. As a safety feature, it only works in the STAT mode so that the memories cannot be cleared while in some other mode.

DISPLAY FORMATS

Even though the calculator has a display and entry limit of eight digits, the internal display register holds calculated results to 11 digits for greater accuracy in subsequent calculation. The value displayed is rounded to eight digits.

In addition to the standard eight-digit floating decimal display, there are several other display formats available to increase the versatility of the calculator.

[EE]—Scientific Notation Key

Many scientific and engineering calculations involve very large or small numbers which can be awkward to manipulate. Scientific notation makes these values easier to handle. Any number can be expressed in scientific notation as a base value (mantissa) times 10 raised to some power (exponent). For example, the value 1,050,000 is expressed as 1.05×10^6 in scientific notation. The sign ($+$ or $-$) of the exponent indicates where the decimal point is placed when the number is written in standard form. A positive exponent indicates that the decimal point shifts to the right when the number is displayed in standard format, and a negative exponent indicates that it shifts to the left. The value of the exponent gives the number of places the decimal point is to be moved. The following table shows some numbers expressed in both standard form and scientific notation.

Standard Notation	Scientific Notation
6,789	6.789×10^3
.0000000021	2.1×10^{-9}
$-16,389,043$	-1.6389043×10^7
8.775	8.775×10^0

Your calculator's scientific notation allows you to use numbers as small as $\pm 1 \times 10^{-99}$ and as large as $\pm 9.9999999 \times 10^{99}$. Numbers smaller than $\pm 1 \times 10^{-7}$ and larger than $\pm 9.9999999 \times 10^{7}$ must be entered into the calculator in scientific notation. If calculations exceed these limits, the results are automatically displayed in scientific notation.

To enter a number in scientific notation, first enter the mantissa, pressing [+/−] if it is negative. Press [EE] and "00" appears at the right of the display. Then enter the exponent, pressing [+/−] if it is negative. If you press a wrong digit key when entering the exponent, press the correct digits and the calculator replaces the old digits with the last digits entered.

Example: Suppose you wanted to enter 6.023×10^{23} but accidentally press the exponent digits in the reverse order.

Press	Display	Comments
[ON/C] [ON/C]	0	Clear display and pending operations
6.023 [EE] 32	6.023 32	The exponent digits are reversed
3	6.023 23	The new entry shifts the exponents and corrects the error

Regardless of how a mantissa is entered in scientific notation, the calculator normalizes the number, displaying a single digit to the left of the decimal point, when any function or operation key is pressed.

After pressing the [EE] key, all results are displayed in scientific notation. To remove the scientific notation format or convert a number to standard form, press [INV] [EE]. Scientific notation is also removed by [ON/C], [2nd] [INV] [Eng], or turning the calculator off and back on. If the number displayed is outside the range $\pm 1 \times 10^{-7}$ to $\pm 9.9999999 \times 10^{7}$, the calculator returns to the standard format only when a calculated result or entry is in the displayable range.

SECTION 2—DATA ENTRY AND CLEARING KEYS

Example: Enter 32.5×10^4 in scientific notation and change it to standard notation.

Press	Display	Comments
ON/C ON/C	0	Clear display and pending operations
32.5 EE 4	32.5 04	Entry
=	3.25 05	Scientific notation
INV EE	325000	Standard notation

Data entered in standard form may be mixed with data in scientific notation for quicker calculations. The calculator converts the standard numbers and displays the results in scientific notation.

Example: $3.2 \times 10^3 + 12575.321 = 15775.321$

Press	Display	Comments
ON/C ON/C	0	Clear display and pending operations
3.2 EE 3	3.2 03	Enter first number
+ 12575.321	12575.321	Add second number
=	1.5775321 04	Result in scientific notation
INV EE	15775.321	Convert result to standard notation

2nd Eng —Engineering Notation Key

Engineering notation is a modified form of scientific notation that allows easier interpretation of technical calculations. Numbers expressed in engineering notation are displayed as a mantissa times 10 raised to a power that is a multiple of three. This allows more convenient handling of metric and engineering units such as kilometers (meters $\times 10^3$), megawatts (watts $\times 10^6$), and milliseconds (seconds $\times 10^{-3}$).

After pressing the 2nd Eng key, all results are displayed in engineering notation. Regardless of how a number is entered (standard format or scientific notation), the calculator normalizes the number, displaying an exponent which is a multiple of three and a mantissa with one, two, or three digits to the left of the decimal point, when any function or operation key is pressed. To remove the engineering notation format or convert a number to standard form, press INV 2nd Eng. If the number displayed is outside the range ±1 × 10^{-7} to ±9.9999999 × 10^7, the calculator displays the number in scientific notation and returns to the standard format only when a result or entry is in the displayable range. Engineering notation is also removed by turning the calculator off and back on.

Example: Enter 32.5 × 10^4 in engineering notation and change it to standard notation.

Press	Display	Comments
ON/C ON/C	0	Clear display and pending operations
32.5 EE 4	32.5 04	Entry
2nd Eng	325 03	Set engineering notation
INV 2nd Eng	325000	Standard notation

2nd Fix n—Fix Decimal Key

In some calculations, you may wish to display a fixed number of digits following the decimal point in standard, scientific, or engineering notation. Pressing 2nd Fix n directs the calculator to round the display to n decimal places. The internal display register still retains the full 11 digit accuracy for use in subsequent calculations.

Fixed decimal format can be used in conjunction with either scientific or engineering notation. When used with these, 2nd Fix n sets the number of decimal places displayed in the mantissa.

If the calculator is in the fixed-decimal format and not in scientific or engineering notation and a calculated result exceeds ±9.9999999 × 10^7 or goes below ±1 × 10^{-7}, the display automatically converts to scientific notation and the fixed-decimal format is ignored. The display returns to the fixed-decimal format when scientific notation is no longer necessary. If the calculator is already in scientific or engineering notation, the fixed-decimal format is retained and the number of decimal places displayed in the mantissa is fixed.

SECTION 2—DATA ENTRY AND CLEARING KEYS

Reset the calculator to the floating decimal point with [INV] [2nd] **Fix**, or [2nd] **Fix** [8], or [2nd] **Fix** [9], or by turning the calculator off and back on.

Example: Display 500÷3, rounded to 6, 2, and 0 decimal places, in both standard notation and scientific notation. Then return to standard notation with a floating decimal point.

Press	Display	Comments
[ON/c] [ON/c]	0	Clear display and pending operations
500 [÷] 3 [=]	166.66667	Result of division
[2nd] **Fix** 6	166.66667	Fix decimal to 6 places. Only 5 can be shown
[2nd] **Fix** 2	166.67	Fix decimal to 2 places
[2nd] **Fix** 0	167	Fix decimal to 0 places
[INV] [2nd] **Fix**	166.66667	Restore floating decimal point
[EE]	1.6666667 02	Enter scientific notation
[2nd] **Fix** 6	1.666667 02	Fix decimal to 6 places
[2nd] **Fix** 2	1.67 02	Fix decimal to 2 places
[2nd] **Fix** 0	2 02	Fix decimal to 0 places
[INV] [EE]	167	Leave scientific notation
[INV] [2nd] **Fix**	166.66667	Restore floating decimal point

Note that while the displayed value is rounded to the desired format, the internal value is unaffected.

Section 3—Mathematical Functions

The keys discussed in this Section all perform tasks that are frequently needed in mathematical and scientific operations.

NOTE: Limits on the range and accuracy of these keys are discussed in Appendix D. For information on how these keys operate in the complex number mode, see the *Complex Number Keys Section* of this chapter.

⊞, ⊟, ⊠, ⊡, ⊜—ARITHMETIC KEYS

The basic arithmetic operations of addition, subtraction, multiplication and division are performed with these five keys. The equals key completes all pending operations and readies the calculator for new calculations.

Several operations can be combined in one expression and entered into the calculator as written from left to right. The calculator has a special feature called the Algebraic Operating System to sort the operations and perform them in the correct order.

AOS™ ALGEBRAIC OPERATING SYSTEM

The AOS™ Algebraic Operating System used in the normal calculation and statistics modes allows entering numbers and combined operations into the calculator in the same order in which they are written mathematically. Combined operations are performed following the universally accepted rules of the algebraic hierarchy which assign priorities to the various mathematical operations. Without such a fixed set of rules, expressions with several operations could have more than one correct interpretation. For example, the expression

$$5 + 4 \times 3 - 2$$

could have several different results. However, the rules of the algebraic hierarchy state that multiplications and divisions should be performed before additions and subtractions. Using these priorities, the calculator finds the correct solution is 15. The complete algebraic hierarchy, in descending order of priority, is:

1. The following perform the indicated function on the displayed value immediately: trigonometric and hyperbolic and their inverses, reciprocal, square, square root, factorial, integer part, absolute value, fractional part, D-R-G and DMS-DD conversions, combinations, permutations, percent, logarithm, and antilogarithm keys
2. The percent change key
3. The universal powers and roots keys
4. Multiplication and division keys
5. Addition and subtraction keys
6. The equals key ⌐=⌐ completes all pending operations

NOTE: The following keys remove any pending calculations: ⌐2nd⌐ ⌐P↔R⌐; ⌐Σ+⌐; ⌐2nd⌐ ⌐Σ−⌐; ⌐2nd⌐ ⌐Mean⌐; ⌐2nd⌐ ⌐σn⌐; ⌐2nd⌐ ⌐σn-1⌐; and ⌐2nd⌐ ⌐b/a⌐. The complex number mode uses the chain arithmetic operating system, see the *Complex Number Keys Section* of this chapter for information.

The keys on the right side of the calculator are positioned to help you to remember the AOS hierarchy.

⌐yˣ⌐
⌐÷⌐
⌐×⌐
⌐−⌐
⌐+⌐
⌐=⌐

Operations with the same priority in an expression are performed left to right. To illustrate the Algebraic Operating System, consider this example.

Example: $4 \div 5^2 \times 7 + 3 \times .5^{\cos 60°} = 3.2413203$

Press ⌐DRG⌐ until neither RAD or GRAD is in the display. This indicates that the calculator is in the degree mode.

Press	Display	Comments
[ON/c] [ON/c]	0	Clear display and pending operations
4 [÷] 5	5	The division is pending
[x^2]	25	Special function [x^2] is performed immediately
[X]	0.16	First division performed, multiplication pending
7 [+]	1.12	Multiplication performed, addition pending
3 [X]	3	Second multiplication pending
.5 [y^x]	0.5	Universal exponential pending
60 [cos]	0.5	Special function performed immediately
[=]	3.2413203	Equals sign completes all pending operations

NOTE: If an incorrect operation is entered while there are pending calculations, it is safest to press [ON/c] [ON/c] and restart the problem.

[( ], [ )]—PARENTHESES KEYS

Some calculations require specifying the exact order in which numbers and operations are to be grouped. Placing a series of numbers and operations in parentheses indicates that they are to be evaluated first instead of in the order directed by the normal algebraic hierarchy. Within each set of parentheses, the calculator operates according to the rules of the algebraic hierarchy. Use the parentheses if there is any doubt about how the calculator will handle an expression. The parentheses keys produce an error message if pressed in the complex number mode. See the *Complex Number Keys Section* for information.

Example: $7 \times (3 + 4) = 49$

Press	Display	Comments
[ON/c] [ON/c]	0	Clear display and pending operations
7 [X] [( ] 3 [+] 4 [ )]	7	Addition result, multiplication pending
[=]	49	Result

SECTION 3—MATHEMATICAL FUNCTIONS

The open parenthesis has the additional capability of supplying a missing number.

Example: $4 - (4 + 2) = -2$

Press	Display	Comments
[ON/C] [ON/C]	0	Clear display and pending operations
4 [−] [(] [+]	4	Enters the number 4. The open parenthesis followed by a [+] causes the 4 to be repeated
2 [)] [=]	−2	Answer

The close parenthesis does not supply a missing number. It does, however, complete the operation started with the most recent open parenthesis. If no open parenthesis is pending, the close parenthesis completes all pending operations.

There are limits to how many operations and associated numbers can be pending. As many as fifteen parentheses can be open at any one time and four operations can be pending, but only in the most complex situations will these limits be approached.

You may see equations or expressions written with parentheses used to indicate implied multiplication: $(2+1)(3+2)=15$. The calculator does not perform implied multiplications. You must enter the multiplication sign.

[(] 2 [+] 1 [)] [X] [(] 3 [+] 2 [)] [=]

Here is an example on using parentheses.

Example: Evaluate $\dfrac{(8 + 9) \times -19}{(3 + 10) \div 7} = -173.92308$

In problems of this type, the calculator must evaluate the entire numerator, then divide by the entire denominator. To be sure that this takes place, add an extra set of parentheses around the numerator and denominator.

Press	**Display**	**Comments**
ON/c ON/c	0	Clear display and pending operations
((8 + 9)	17	(8 + 9) displayed
X 19 +/-) ÷	−323	The value of the numerator
((3 + 10		
) ÷ 7)	1.8571429	The value of the denominator
=	−173.92308	The result

1/x — RECIPROCAL KEY

The reciprocal key 1/x divides the displayed number into one. For example, 4 1/x equals 1/4 or .25. Pending operations are not affected by this key.

√x , x² — SQUARE ROOT AND SQUARE KEYS

These keys find the square roots and squares of numbers. They act immediately on the number in the display and do not affect pending calculations.

The square root key √x calculates the square root of the positive number in the display. The square root of negative numbers can be calculated in the complex number mode.

x² calculates the square of the number in the display, multiplying the displayed number by itself.

yˣ , INV yˣ —UNIVERSAL POWER AND ROOT KEYS

yˣ is the universal power key. It raises any positive number to any power. Negative numbers can be raised to any power in the complex number mode. See the *Complex Number Keys Section* of this chapter for more information. For information on the accuracy of the universal power function, see Appendix D.

To use this key:

- Enter the number to be raised to a power ("y")
- Press yˣ
- Enter the power ("x")
- Press = or any operator key

SECTION 3—MATHEMATICAL FUNCTIONS

Example: Calculate $3.1897^{4.7343}$

Press	Display	Comments
ON/C ON/C	0	Clear display and pending operations
3.1897 $\boxed{y^x}$	3.1897	"y" value
4.7343	4.7343	"x" value
$\boxed{=}$	242.60674	Result: y^x

The universal root key takes any root of any positive number. The root of negative numbers is allowed in the complex number mode. See the *Complex Number Keys Section* of this chapter for more information.

To use this key:

- Enter the number to take the root of ("y")
- Press $\boxed{INV}$ $\boxed{y^x}$
- Enter the root to be taken ("x")
- Press $\boxed{=}$ or any operator key

Example: Calculate $\sqrt[3.871]{21.496}$

Press	Display	Comments
ON/C ON/C	0	Clear display and pending operations
21.496 $\boxed{INV}$ $\boxed{y^x}$	21.496	"y" value
3.871	3.871	"x" value
$\boxed{=}$	2.2089685	Result: $\sqrt[x]{y}$

$\boxed{\ln x}$, $\boxed{\log}$, $\boxed{\text{INV}}$ $\boxed{\ln x}$, $\boxed{\text{INV}}$ $\boxed{\log}$—LOGARITHM AND ANTILOGARITHM KEYS

Logarithms are mathematical functions used in a variety of technical and theoretical calculations. In addition, they form an important part of many mathematical "models" of natural phenomena. The logarithm keys give immediate access to the "log" of any number without having to locate it in a table.

The natural logarithm key $\boxed{\ln x}$ displays the natural logarithm (base e = 2.7182818) of the number in the display. The number in the display must be positive when in normal calculation mode. In complex number mode the logarithm of negative numbers is allowed.

The common logarithm key $\boxed{\log}$ displays the common logarithm (base 10) of the number in the display. The number in the display must be positive when in normal calculation mode. In complex number mode the logarithm of negative numbers is allowed.

The antilogarithm keys raise e and 10 to the power of the number in the display. $\boxed{\text{INV}}$ $\boxed{\ln x}$ raises e to the power in the display. $\boxed{\text{INV}}$ $\boxed{\log}$ raises 10 to the power in the display.

The logarithm and antilogarithm functions do not affect pending operations when pressed.

Example: Calculate log 15.32, ln 203.451, $e^{-.69315}$, 10^{π}

Press	Display	Comments
$\boxed{\text{ON/c}}$ $\boxed{\text{ON/c}}$	0	Clear display and pending operations
15.32 $\boxed{\log}$	1.1852588	
203.451 $\boxed{\ln x}$	5.3154252	
.69315 $\boxed{+/-}$ $\boxed{\text{INV}}$ $\boxed{\ln x}$	0.4999986	
$\boxed{\pi}$ $\boxed{\text{INV}}$ $\boxed{\log}$	1385.4557	

SECTION 3—MATHEMATICAL FUNCTIONS

[sin], [cos], [tan], [INV] [sin], [INV] [cos], [INV] [tan]—
TRIGONOMETRIC KEYS

The trigonometric keys [sin], [cos], and [tan] calculate the sine, cosine, and tangent of the angle in the display, with the angle measured in the units selected with the [DRG], [INV] [DRG], [2nd] [DRG►], or [INV] [2nd] [DRG►] keys. For information on selecting the angular mode, see the *Conversion Keys Section* of this chapter. The trigonometric functions relate the angles and sides of a right triangle as shown below.

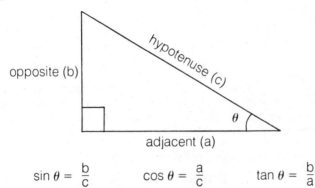

$$\sin \theta = \frac{b}{c} \qquad \cos \theta = \frac{a}{c} \qquad \tan \theta = \frac{b}{a}$$

The inverse functions of the trigonometric keys give the angle, in the units selected, whose sine, cosine, or tangent is in the display. [INV] [sin] calculates the arcsine ($\sin^{-1}$), [INV] [cos] calculates the arccosine ($\cos^{-1}$), and [INV] [tan] calculates the arctangent ($\tan^{-1}$).

The trigonometric and inverse trigonometric functions do not affect pending operations when pressed.

Note the following ranges for the use of the inverse trigonometric functions.

Arc Function	Range of Resultant Angle
arcsin x	0 to 90°, $\pi \div 2$ radians, or 100G
arcsin −x	0 to −90°, $-\pi \div 2$ radians, or −100G
arccos x	0 to 90°, $\pi \div 2$ radians, or 100G
arccos −x	90° to 180°, $\pi \div 2$ to π radians, or 100G to 200G
arctan x	0 to 90°, $\pi \div 2$ radians, or 100G
arctan −x	0 to −90°, $-\pi \div 2$ radians, or −100G

⌈hyp⌉—HYPERBOLIC FUNCTION KEY

Preceding one of the trigonometric keys with the ⌈hyp⌉ key calculates the hyperbolic sine (sinh), hyperbolic cosine (cosh), hyperbolic tangent (tanh), hyperbolic arcsine (sinh⁻¹), hyperbolic arccosine (cosh⁻¹), and hyperbolic arctangent (tanh⁻¹) of the number in the display. These functions operate in a fashion similar to the trigonometric functions except the angular mode (degree, radian, grad) has no effect on hyperbolic functions. The following illustrate the use of the hyperbolic function key.

Keys Pressed	Result
⌈hyp⌉ ⌈sin⌉	Hyperbolic sine (sinh)
⌈INV⌉ ⌈hyp⌉ ⌈sin⌉	Hyperbolic arcsine (arcsinh or sinh⁻¹)
⌈hyp⌉ ⌈INV⌉ ⌈sin⌉	Hyperbolic arcsine (arcsinh or sinh⁻¹)

NOTE: The key sequence ⌈hyp⌉ ⌈2nd⌉ is the same as if just ⌈2nd⌉ had been pressed. The key sequence ⌈2nd⌉ ⌈hyp⌉ is the same as if just ⌈hyp⌉ had been pressed. Pressing ⌈hyp⌉ twice returns the following trigonometric function to its primary function.

Example: Find the hyperbolic tangent of $100 \div 3.3 \times 10^2$.

Press	Display	Comments
⌈ON/C⌉ ⌈ON/C⌉	0	Clear display and pending operations
100 ⌈÷⌉ 3.3 ⌈EE⌉	3.3 00	
2 ⌈=⌉	3.030303−01	Intermediate result
⌈hyp⌉ ⌈tan⌉	2.940833−01	Answer in scientific notation
⌈INV⌉ ⌈EE⌉	0.2940833	Answer in standard notation

The hyperbolic and inverse hyperbolic functions do not affect pending operations.

Note the following restrictions on the limits of the inverse hyperbolic functions:

Arcsinh x must have a value such that $-10^{50} < x < -10^{-50}$, $10^{-50} < x < 10^{50}$, x=0.
Arccosh x must have a value such that $1 \le x < 10^{50}$.
Arctanh x must have a value such that $-1 < x < 1$.

SECTION 3—MATHEMATICAL FUNCTIONS

[2nd] [Abs], [2nd] [Intg], [2nd] [Frac]—NUMBER PORTION KEYS

[2nd] [Abs] calculates and displays the absolute value of the number in the display. The absolute value of a number is the magnitude of the number regardless of the sign. Thus the result of [2nd] [Abs] is always a positive number.

[2nd] [Intg] displays the integer part of the number in the display register and discards the fractional part. See the following note.

[2nd] [Frac] displays the fractional part of the number in the display register and discards the integer part. See the following note.

NOTE: The [2nd] [Intg] and [2nd] [Frac] keys operate on the 11 internal digits in the display register, not the 8 digits shown in the display. This means that when [2nd] [Intg] is pressed and 4.9999999999 is in the display register internally (which rounds to a value of 5 in the display), that 4 will be the integer that remains in the display. Similarly, [2nd] [Frac] will give a display of 1, with the actual value being .9999999999.

[2nd] [x!], [2nd] [nPr], [2nd] [nCr]—FACTORIAL, PERMUTATIONS, AND COMBINATIONS KEYS

The factorial, permutations, and combinations keys act on the number in the display, and do not affect calculations in progress. The [2nd] [x!] key calculates and displays the factorial of the number. The factorial of any integer x is written x!, and is equal to $(1 \times 2 \times 3 \times ... \times x)$. 0! is equal to 1 by definition. The calculator can determine the factorial of any integer less than 70.

The [2nd] [nPr] key determines the possible permutations (number of arrangements) of n items taken r at a time. This is usually written as $P(^n_r)$. The calculator actually calculates $\dfrac{n!}{(n-r)!}$.

The [2nd] [nCr] key determines the possible combinations of n items taken r at a time. This is usually written as $C(^n_r)$. The calculator actually calculates $\dfrac{n!}{(n-r)! \times r!}$.

The values of n and r are entered as n.rrr. For instance, to enter 5 items taken 2 at a time, enter 5.002. If you enter 5.02, the calculator determines 5 items taken 20 at a time. If you enter 5.2, the calculator determines 5 items taken 200 at a time. "Error" is displayed if r is entered as more than three digits. Note that the permutations and combinations keys work on the display value. Thus entering 5.0021567 [2nd] [Fix] 3 would be a valid key sequence calculating 5 items taken 2 at a time.

Example: How many possible different thirteen card bridge hands are there? In this case n is 52 and r is 13.

Press	Display	Comments
[ON/c] [ON/c]	0	Clear display and pending operations
52.013 [2nd] [nCr]	6.3501356 11	Combinations

Example: The individual books of a 10 volume set of Shakespeare are placed next to each other on a shelf at random. How many possible orderings of the volumes are there? In this case n is 10 and r is 10.

Press	Display	Comments
[ON/c] [ON/c]	0	Clear display and pending operations
10.01 [2nd] [nPr]	3628800	Permutations

[%], [2nd] [Δ%] — PERCENT AND PERCENT CHANGE KEYS

These keys are useful for a wide variety of business and domestic percentage calculations.

The [%] key converts the number in the display to a decimal percent by multiplying it by 0.01. If you enter 43.9 and press [%], 0.439 is displayed.

The real power of the [%] key is demonstrated when it is used with an operation key. This allows add-on and discount as well as straight and inverted percentage calculations. The rules for using the [%] key in these situations are as follows.

m [+] n [%] [=] adds n% of m to m
m [−] n [%] [=] subtracts n% of m from m
m [×] n [%] [=] multiplies m by n%
m [÷] n [%] [=] divides m by n%

SECTION 3—MATHEMATICAL FUNCTIONS

The [2nd] [Δ%] (change percent or delta percent) key calculates the percentage change between two values. This type of calculation is often used in business and everyday situations.

Example: Suppose your car has been getting 17.0 miles per gallon (call this x). After tuning it, mileage increases to 19.8 MPG (y). What is the percent increase?

To calculate this, enter y, press [2nd] [Δ%], enter x, press [=], and the percentage change is displayed. (The calculator figures $\frac{y - x}{x} \times 100$.)

Press	Display	Comments
[ON/c] [ON/c]	0	Clear display and pending operations
19.8 [2nd] [Δ%]	19.8	Enter new mileage (y)
17	17	Enter old mileage (x)
[=]	16.470588	Percent change

[K] — CONSTANT KEY

The [K] key stores a number and an operation for use in repetitive calculations. Once the number and operation are stored, key in the values you want them to work on, press [=], and the answer is displayed. Calculations using the [K] feature can be repeated as often as needed. Here is how it works.

- Enter the operation
- Enter the repetitive number m
- Press [K]
- Press [=]

From then on

- Enter the number to be operated on
- Press [=]

The $\boxed{K}$ feature works in the following way with certain operations keys on the calculator.

$\boxed{+}$ m $\boxed{K}$ $\boxed{=}$	adds m to each subsequent entry
$\boxed{-}$ m $\boxed{K}$ $\boxed{=}$	subtracts m from each subsequent entry
$\boxed{\times}$ m $\boxed{K}$ $\boxed{=}$	multiplies each subsequent entry by m
$\boxed{\div}$ m $\boxed{K}$ $\boxed{=}$	divides each subsequent entry by m
$\boxed{y^x}$ m $\boxed{K}$ $\boxed{=}$	raises each subsequent entry to the mth power, giving y^m
$\boxed{INV}$ $\boxed{y^x}$ m $\boxed{K}$ $\boxed{=}$	takes the mth root of each subsequent entry, giving $\sqrt[m]{y}$
$\boxed{2nd}$ $\boxed{\Delta\%}$ m $\boxed{K}$ $\boxed{=}$	calculates the percentage change between each subsequent entry s and m, computing $\frac{s-m}{m} \times 100$.

You may enter $\boxed{K}$ while doing the first in a series of problems.

Example: Multiply 2, 4, 6, and 8 by π (pi).

Press	**Display**	**Comments**
$\boxed{ON/C}$ $\boxed{ON/C}$	0	Clear display and pending operations
2 $\boxed{\times}$ $\boxed{\pi}$ $\boxed{K}$	3.1415927	π
$\boxed{=}$	6.2831853	2π
4 $\boxed{=}$	12.566371	4π
6 $\boxed{=}$	18.849556	6π
8 $\boxed{=}$	25.132741	8π

Pressing $\boxed{ON/C}$ after $\boxed{=}$, $\boxed{OFF}$, any of the operation keys listed above, or the close parenthesis key removes the automatic constant. The constant key produces an error message if pressed in the complex number mode. See the *Complex Number Keys Section* for information.

SECTION 3—MATHEMATICAL FUNCTIONS

MEMORY OPERATIONS

In the normal calculation mode, there are seven user data memories, numbered 0 through 6, which can be used to store intermediate results or long values. In the statistics mode, only two memories are allowed while in the complex number mode three memories can be used. The following keys and operations allow manipulation of the numbers in the user data memories. For complex number memory operations, see the *Complex Number Keys Section* of this chapter.

[2nd] CM—Clear Memories Key

The [2nd] CM key clears all the user data memories. The display and statistical registers are not affected.

[STO] m—Store Memory Key

The [STO] m key stores the value shown in the display in user data memory m. For instance, the key sequence 3 [STO] 1 stores the value 3 in user data memory 1.

[RCL] m—Recall Memory Key

The [RCL] m key recalls to the display the number in user data memory m. For instance, the key sequence [RCL] 2 recalls to the display the number that was in user data memory 2.

[EXC] m—Exchange Memory Key

The [EXC] m key exchanges the value in the display with the value in user data memory m. For instance, the key sequence 7 [EXC] 3 stores the value 7 in user data memory 3 and displays the value that was stored in user data memory 3.

Note that in the above descriptions m may have the values 0 to 6 for normal calculations and 0 and 1 for statistical calculations.

MEMORY ARITHMETIC

If an operation is to be performed on a number stored in a user data memory with the result of that operation stored back in that memory, it can be done using the memory arithmetic feature of your calculator. Without the memory arithmetic feature, the number would have to be recalled, the operation performed, and the result stored in memory again. The memory arithmetic feature of your calculator allows you to enter a value, press [STO], enter the operation to be performed, and enter the number of the user data memory in which to store the result. These key sequences are used to accumulate results from a series of independent calculations. The displayed number and calculations in progress are not affected. To use these sequences:

- Enter the number that is to operate on the memory value
- Press [STO]
- Enter the operation to be performed
- Enter the number of the memory to be used

NOTE: Because of the calculator's Constant Memory™ feature, the user data memories are not cleared when the calculator is turned off. Be sure to press [ON/C] [STO] m initially to clear the desired user data memory before using any of the following key sequences. [2nd] [CM] clears all available user data memories. The memory arithmetic feature is not available in the complex number mode and the key sequence given above will produce an error message if pressed. See the *Complex Number Keys Section* of this chapter for more information.

SECTION 3—MATHEMATICAL FUNCTIONS

The memory arithmetic feature works in the following way with certain operations keys on the calculator.

[STO] [+] m algebraically adds the displayed value to the contents of user data memory m.

[STO] [−] m algebraically subtracts the displayed value from the contents of user data memory m.

[STO] [X] m multiplies the contents of user data memory m by the displayed value.

[STO] [÷] m divides the contents of user data memory m by the displayed value.

[STO] [y^x] m raises the contents of user data memory m to the power in the display.

[STO] [INV] [y^x] m takes the root indicated by the number in the display of the value in user data memory m.

[STO] [2nd] [Δ%] m determines the percent change from the number in the display to the value in user data memory m.

Example:		$28.3 \times 7 = 198.1$
		$173 + 16 = 189$
		$31 - 42 + 7.8 = -3.2$
		Total 383.9

Press	**Display**	**Comments**
[ON/c] [ON/c] [STO] 0	0	Clear display, pending operations, and memory 0
28.3 [X] 7 [=] [STO] [+] 0	198.1	Result of first problem added to memory 0
173 [+] 16 [=] [STO] [+] 0	189	Result of second problem added to memory 0
31 [−] 42 [+] 7.8 [=] [STO] [+] 0	−3.2	Result of third problem added to memory 0
[RCL] 0	383.9	Recall sum of the problems from memory 0

Section 4—Conversion Keys

The TI-54 allows the entry of angular measures in degrees, radians, or grads with measurements easily convertible from one to the other. Your calculator also has keys to convert from degrees/minutes/seconds format to decimal degrees and from the polar coordinate system to the rectangular coordinate system.

[DRG], [INV] [DRG], [2nd] [DRG►], [INV] [2nd] [DRG►]—DEGREE, RADIAN, AND GRAD KEYS

The calculator handles a variety of calculations involving angles, such as the trigonometric functions and polar/rectangular conversions. When performing these calculations, select any one of the three common units for angular measure.

Degrees are each equal to $1 \div 360$ of a circle. A right angle equals 90°.

Radians are each equal to $1 \div 2\pi$ of a circle. A right angle equals $\pi \div 2$ radians.

Grads are each equal to $1 \div 400$ of a circle. A right angle equals 100 grads.

The calculator is always in degree mode when it is turned on indicated by the absence of both RAD and GRAD in the display. Pressing [DRG] changes it to radian mode, indicated by RAD in the display. Pressing [DRG] again changes it to grad mode, indicated by GRAD in the display. Pressing [DRG] again returns the calculator to degree mode. You may also go through the modes in reverse order—from degrees to grads to radians and back to degrees—by pressing [INV] [DRG].

The [2nd] [DRG►] key also changes the mode displayed, and additionally converts the number in the display to the new units. Thus 90 in the degree mode followed by [2nd] [DRG►] changes the mode to radians and the display to 1.5707963 ($\pi \div 2$). Pressing [2nd] [DRG►] again changes the mode to grads and the display to 100. You may also go through the modes and values in reverse order—from degrees to grads to radians and back to degrees—by pressing the [INV] [2nd] [DRG►] key.

SECTION 4—CONVERSION KEYS

[2nd] [DMS-DD], [INV] [2nd] [DMS-DD]—DEGREES/MINUTES/SECONDS TO DECIMAL DEGREES CONVERSION KEYS

There are two ways of representing an angle in degrees. One method is to use the decimal degree format DD.dd as required by the calculator for trigonometric functions. Here DD represents the integer portion of the angle and dd represents the fraction portion written as a decimal. Up to 8 digits may be entered.

The second method is to use the degrees/minutes/seconds format DD.MMSSss. Again DD represents the whole angle. MM represents minutes and SS denotes seconds. For greater accuracy, fractional seconds may be entered in the ss position. The decimal point separates degrees from minutes.

To convert from the degrees/minutes/seconds format to decimal degrees, enter the angle in the display as DD.MMSSss and press [2nd] [DMS-DD]. Pressing [INV] [2nd] [DMS-DD] reverses the conversion process and converts decimal degrees to degrees, minutes, and seconds. Two digits should always be entered for minutes and two for seconds. Trailing zeros need not be entered.

Example: Convert 3°1'30.456'' to decimal degrees and back.

Press	Display	Comments
[ON/c] [ON/c]	0	Clear display and pending operations
3.0130456 [2nd] [DMS-DD]	3.0251267	Answer in decimal degrees
[INV] [2nd] [DMS-DD]	3.0130456	Answer returned to degrees/minutes/seconds

The same procedure is followed to convert from hours, minutes, seconds to decimal hours and vice versa.

[2nd] [P→R] , [INV] [2nd] [P→R] —**POLAR/RECTANGULAR
CONVERSION KEYS**

The rectangular coordinate system describes where points are
placed on a grid by a pair of numbers. The first, the x-coordinate,
describes the distance of the point from the y-axis, which is a
vertical line. The second, the y-coordinate, describes the distance of
the point from the x-axis, which is a horizontal line. The following
shows the point described in rectangular coordinates as (3,4).

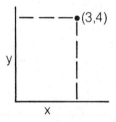

The polar system of coordinates describes a point in terms of a line
drawn from a center to the point. It also uses a pair of numbers. The
first number is the length of the line, labeled r. The second is the
angle the line is from the horizontal, labeled theta (θ). The following
shows the same point, but described as (5,53.130102°).

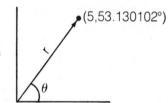

The conversion from polar to rectangular coordinates and back
involves some detailed arithmetic. Fortunately, the calculator can
perform these calculations.

To convert from polar to rectangular coordinates, follow these steps:

Enter the r value
Press [x:y]
Enter the θ value
Press [2nd] [P→R]
The y-coordinate is displayed.
Press [x:y]
The x-coordinate is displayed.

To convert from rectangular to polar coordinates, follow these steps:

Enter the x-coordinate
Press [x:y]
Enter the y-coordinate
Press [INV] [2nd] [P→R]

The θ value is displayed in the units selected by the [DRG] key.
Press [x:y]

The r value is displayed.

The range of θ is from +180° to −180°, π to −π radians, or 200 to −200 grads. When converting the ordered pair of numbers (0,0), the θ value has arbitrarily been chosen as 90°, or π/2 radians, or 100 grads.

Note that the [2nd] [P→R] key clears any pending operations.

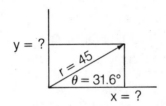

Example: Convert r = 45 meters, θ = 31.6 degrees to rectangular coordinates.

Press [DRG] until neither RAD or GRAD is in the display. This indicates that the calculator is in the degree mode.

Press	Display	Comments
[ON/c] [ON/c]	0	Clear display and pending operations
45 [x:y] 31.6 [2nd] [P→R]	23.579366	y-coordinate value
[x:y]	38.327712	x-coordinate value

Section 5—Complex Number Keys

Complex numbers are defined so that each complex number z is an ordered pair of real numbers (x,y), which can be written as (x,0) + (0,y) or x + [(0,1) × y]. The ordered pair of numbers (0,1) is given the special designation i, or j when working with electrical circuits. Thus (x,y) can be written as x + iy. This expression is called the rectangular form of complex numbers. In the rectangular form of expression, x is called the real part and y is called the imaginary part of the number. Complex numbers can also be expressed in polar form as r $\underline{/\theta}$. In the polar form of expression, r is called the modulus or absolute value and θ is called the argument of the number. Your calculator can handle both forms of expression. This section describes the fundamentals of working with complex numbers on your calculator. For applications examples of the complex number mode see Chapter 4, *Complex Number Applications.*

COMPLEX NUMBER MODE INDICATORS

When CMPLX is in the display, the calculator is in the complex number mode. The complex number mode is entered when [Img] or [θ] is pressed. When the complex number is in polar form, the polar notation indicator r,θ also appears in the display. Since complex numbers have two parts, real (x) and imaginary (y) or modulus (r) and argument (θ), your calculator has a method to help you identify which part is displayed. Whenever the imaginary part (y) or argument (θ) is in the display, the CMPLX indicator blinks. The indicator stops blinking if the exchange sequence is used to display the real part (x) or the modulus (r), or if a new number is entered, or if an operation key is pressed, or if the display is cleared with [ON/C]. Note that the operations ignored in the complex number mode ([2nd] [Intg], [2nd] [Frac], [2nd] [x!], [2nd] [nPr], [2nd] [nCr], trigonometric functions, hyperbolics, and statistical functions) and [2nd] [CM], [2nd] [Fix], [DRG], [2nd] [DRG►], [2nd] [DMS-DD], [EE], and [2nd] [Eng] do not affect the blinking of the indicator. Pressing [INV] [Img] or [INV] [θ] clears the CMPLX indicator along with the r,θ indicator if present, all pending operations, and *imaginary parts* of complex numbers stored in memory, and returns the calculator to normal calculation mode.

SECTION 5—COMPLEX NUMBER KEYS

[ON/C], [2nd] **CM**—CLEARING KEYS

The [ON/C] key is used to clear entries and operations. If a mistake is made while entering the real or imaginary part or r or θ value of a complex number, press the [ON/C] key once and reenter that part again. If an operation key or [Img] or [θ] has been pressed, pressing the [ON/C] key immediately clears all pending operations and the operands entered. Pressing the [ON/C] key twice always clears the display and all pending operations and operands from the calculator.

To clear the three paired user data memories available in the complex number mode, press [2nd] **CM**.

DATA ENTRY

Complex numbers may be entered in either rectangular form, x + iy, or polar form, r/θ. The following section describes the rectangular method of entry first and then the polar method. Data in rectangular form may be mixed with data in polar form for quicker calculations. While in the complex number mode, the data entry keys ([0] to [9], [π], [·], [+/−]) and display format keys ([EE], [2nd] **Eng**, [2nd] **Fix**, and their inverses) operate in the same way as in the normal calculation mode.

Rectangular Form

To enter a number in rectangular form, enter the imaginary part of the complex number and press [Img]. The calculator stores the imaginary part and enters the complex number mode with the CMPLX indicator and 0 shown in the display. Next enter the real part of the complex number. *Note that the method of entering data in the complex number mode is the opposite of the method of entering paired data in the other modes.*

After entering the complex number, you can press [EXC] [Img] to display or check the imaginary part of the number. The CMPLX indicator blinks to indicate that the imaginary part is in the display. Press [EXC] [Img] again to return the real part to the display. The CMPLX indicator stops blinking.

Important: Be sure that you return the real part of the complex number to the display after checking the imaginary part and before performing any operations. The value in the display just before an operation key is pressed is assumed to be the real part of the number even if [EXC] [Img] was pressed and the CMPLX indicator is blinking. Pressing [EXC] [Img] once and pressing an operation key swaps the imaginary and real parts in subsequent calculations.

Example: Enter 5 + 3i

Press	Display	Comments
[ON/c] [ON/c]	0	Clear display and pending operations
3	3	Enter imaginary part of complex number
[Img]	0	The calculator stores the imaginary part and enters the complex number mode as indicated by CMPLX in the display. Zero is shown as the real part
5	5	Enter the real part of the complex number
[EXC] [Img]	3	Display imaginary part of the number. CMPLX blinks to indicate the imaginary part is in the display
[EXC] [Img]	5	Return real part to display. CMPLX stops blinking

Polar Form

To enter a number in polar form, enter the θ value and press $\boxed{\theta}$. The θ value may be entered in degrees, radians, or grads. For information on selecting the angular mode setting, see Conversions later in this section. Pressing the $\boxed{\theta}$ key stores the θ value and places the calculator in the complex number mode with the CMPLX and r,θ indicators and 0 shown in the display. Next enter the r value. *Note that the method of entering r and θ in the complex number mode is the opposite of that used in polar to rectangular conversions in the other modes.*

After entering the complex number in polar form, you can press $\boxed{\text{EXC}}$ $\boxed{\theta}$ to display or check the θ value. The CMPLX indicator blinks to indicate that the θ value is in the display. Press $\boxed{\text{EXC}}$ $\boxed{\theta}$ again to return the r value to the display. The CMPLX indicator stops blinking.

Important: Be sure that you return the r value to the display after checking the θ value and before performing any operations. The value in the display just before an operation key is pressed is assumed to be the r value, even if $\boxed{\text{EXC}}$ $\boxed{\theta}$ was pressed and the CMPLX indicator is blinking. Pressing $\boxed{\text{EXC}}$ $\boxed{\theta}$ just once and pressing an operation key swaps the r value and the θ value in subsequent calculations.

Remember that all mathematical and memory operations automatically convert complex numbers entered in polar form to rectangular form causing the r,θ indicator to be removed from the display.

Example: Enter 6.5 $\underline{/-\pi/2}$ radians

Press DRG until RAD is in the display. This indicates that the calculator is in the radian mode.

Press	Display	Comments
ON/C ON/C	0	Clear display and pending operations. Calculator is still in the complex number mode as indicated by CMPLX in the display
π ÷ 2 = +/−	−1.5707963	Calculate the θ value
θ	0	The calculator stores the θ value and CMPLX and r,θ indicators show that the calculator is in the complex number mode with the number in polar form
6.5	6.5	Enter the r value
EXC θ	−1.5707963	Display the θ value. The CMPLX indicator blinks to indicate that the θ value is in the display
EXC θ	6.5	Return r value to the display. CMPLX stops blinking

Overview of Data Entry

Complex numbers may be entered in rectangular form using the Img key or in polar form using the θ key. Enter the imaginary part (θ value), press the Img (θ) key, and then enter the real part (r value). If a number has only a real part, Img or θ does not need to be pressed except for the first time complex number mode entry is necessary. Remember that when changing from normal calculation mode to complex number mode the pending operations are not retained. Real number operations performed in the complex number mode use chain arithmetic. See the Chain Arithmetic section for more information.

SECTION 5—COMPLEX NUMBER KEYS

Example: Enter the real value 13 in the complex number mode.

Press	Display	Comments
[ON/c] [ON/c]	0	Clear display and pending operations. If r,θ indicator was in the display, it is cleared. CMPLX indicator remains in the display
13	13	Enter the real value 13
[EXC] [Img]	0	Display imaginary part of number. CMPLX blinks
[EXC] [Img]	13	Return real number to the display. CMPLX stops blinking

If a number has an imaginary part only, enter the imaginary value and press [Img]. Since the display always shows a zero after the [Img] key is pressed, the zero for the real part does not have to be entered.

Example: Enter −15i

Press	Display	Comments
[ON/c] [ON/c]	0	Clear display and pending operations
15 [+/−]	−15	Enter the imaginary number
[Img]	0	Since 0 is in the display, there is no need to enter the 0 for the real part
[EXC] [Img]	−15	Display imaginary part of the number. CMPLX blinks
[EXC] [Img]	0	Real part of number in the display. CMPLX stops blinking

If you make a mistake and enter the values of the complex number backwards (i.e. you enter the real or modulus and then the imaginary or argument), you may press EXC Img *or* EXC θ *and swap the two parts. Even though the CMPLX indicator blinks, the values are in the proper order and operations may be performed as necessary. Be sure to check that the desired real or r value is in the display before performing operations.*

If the complex number is in rectangular form, the key sequence EXC θ is ignored. Likewise, if the complex number is in polar form, the key sequence EXC Img is ignored.

MATHEMATICAL FUNCTIONS

The keys discussed in this section perform tasks that are frequently needed in mathematical and scientific operations.

+, −, X, ÷, =—Arithmetic Keys

The basic arithmetic operations of addition, subtraction, multiplication and division are performed with these five keys. Each of these keys completes the previously entered operation. The details are discussed in the Chain Arithmetic section below.

Chain Arithmetic

In the complex number mode, the calculator uses chain arithmetic rather than the AOS™ method used in the other modes of the calculator. As each of the binary operations (+, −, X, ÷, y^x, INV y^x) is keyed, it completes the previously entered operation unlike the AOS method which performs operations according to an algebraic hierarchy. Also, the parentheses keys cannot be used in the complex number mode. Therefore, you must be sure to enter the problem in the exact manner in which you want it executed. Data in polar form may be mixed with data in rectangular form for quicker calculations. *The complex numbers entered in polar form are converted to rectangular form when any operation key, unary or binary, is pressed. The results of calculations are always in rectangular form.*

SECTION 5—COMPLEX NUMBER KEYS

Example: Solve $(8\underline{/\pi/4}) - (6 - 8i) \div (12 + 4i) = ?$

Note that the parentheses in the above problem are provided to separate the numbers. They are not entered in the calculator. The parentheses keys produce an error message if pressed in the complex number mode.

Press DRG until RAD is shown in the display. This ensures that the calculator is in the radian mode.

Press	Display	Comments
ON/C ON/C	0	Clear display and pending operations
π ÷ 4 =	0.7853982	Calculate $\pi/4$
θ 8	8	Enter first complex number in polar form. CMPLX and r,θ indicators appear in the display
− *	5.6568542	Complex number is converted to rectangular form when the operation key is pressed, r,θ indicator disappears. Subtraction is pending
8 +/− Img 6	6	Enter second complex number
÷	−0.3431458	Subtraction completed. Division pending
4 Img 12	12	Enter next complex number
=	0.3156854	Division completed. Result is in rectangular form with the real part in the display
EXC Img	1.0328427	Display the imaginary part of the result. CMPLX blinks

*Wait for CALC to disappear from the display before making more entries. Entries made while CALC is in the display are ignored, which may result in a wrong answer.

⌜¹/x⌝—Reciprocal Key

The reciprocal key ⌜¹/x⌝ divides the displayed number into one. It operates immediately on the real or complex number entered preceding it (both the real and imaginary or r and θ parts) and does not affect any pending operation.

⌜√x⌝, ⌜x²⌝—Square Root and Square Keys

These keys find the square roots and squares of numbers. They act immediately on the real or complex number entered just before they were pressed and do not affect a pending operation.

The square root key ⌜√x⌝ calculates the square root of the real or complex number entered just before it was pressed.

⌜x²⌝ calculates the square of the real or complex number entered just before it was pressed, multiplying the number by itself.

⌜yˣ⌝, ⌜INV⌝ ⌜yˣ⌝—Universal Power and Root Keys

⌜yˣ⌝ is the universal power key. It raises any number to any power. To use this key:

- Enter the real or complex number to be raised to a power ("y") in either rectangular or polar form
- Press ⌜yˣ⌝
- Enter the real or complex number power ("x") in either rectangular or polar form
- Press ⌜=⌝ (or ⌜+⌝, ⌜−⌝, ⌜X⌝, ⌜÷⌝, ⌜yˣ⌝, or ⌜INV⌝ ⌜yˣ⌝ if desired).

Note that pressing the ⌜yˣ⌝ key completes the previously pending operation and converts a complex number entered in polar form to rectangular form. The result is always in rectangular form.

SECTION 5—COMPLEX NUMBER KEYS

Example: Calculate $(2 \underline{/45°})^{(3 + 2i)}$

Press DRG until neither RAD or GRAD is seen in the display. This ensures that the calculator is in the degree mode.

Press	Display	Comments
ON/c ON/c	0	Clear display and pending operations
45 θ	0	Enter θ value of complex number
2	2	Enter r value of complex number
y^x	1.4142136	Press universal power key. Polar form is converted to rectangular form with the real part in the display. Be sure to wait until CALC disappears before pressing the next key
2 Img 3	3	Enter power
=	−1.3717212	The equals key completes the operation. The real part of the result is in the display
EXC Img	−0.9402508	Display the imaginary part of the result

The universal root key takes any root of any number when used in the complex number mode. To use this key:

- Enter the real or complex number to take the root of ("y") in either rectangular or polar form
- Press INV y^x
- Enter the real or complex number root to be taken ("x") in either rectangular or polar form
- Press = (or +, −, X, ÷, y^x, or INV y^x if desired)

Note that pressing the INV y^x key sequence completes the previously pending operation and converts a complex number entered in polar form to rectangular form. The result is always in rectangular form.

Example: Calculate $^{4.7}\sqrt{4 + 2i}$

Press	Display	Comments
ON/c ON/c	0	Clear display and pending operations
2 Img 4	4	Enter the complex number to take the root of (y value)
INV yˣ 4.7	4.7	Press the universal root key sequence and enter the root (x value)
=	1.3686451	Result in rectangular form
EXC Img	0.1354544	Display imaginary part of the result

lnx, log, INV lnx, INV log—Logarithm and Antilogarithm Keys

The natural logarithm key lnx calculates the natural logarithm (base e = 2.7182818) of the real or complex number entered just prior to it.

The common logarithm key log calculates the common logarithm (base 10) of the real or complex number entered just prior to it.

The antilogarithm keys raise e and 10 to the power of the real or complex number entered. INV lnx raises e to the power entered. INV log raises 10 to the power entered.

Logarithm and antilogarithm operations do not affect a pending operation.

SECTION 5—COMPLEX NUMBER KEYS

Example: Calculate log $(2 + 3i)$ and $e^{4/30°}$

Press DRG until neither RAD or GRAD is shown in the display. This indicates that the calculator is in the degree mode.

Press	Display	Comments
ON/c ON/c	0	Clear display and pending operations
3 Img 2	2	Enter complex number
log	0.5569717	Real part of log in display
EXC Img	0.4268219	Display imaginary part of log
30 θ 4	4	Enter complex number in polar form
INV lnx	−13.294953	Antilogarithm in rectangular form with real part in display
EXC Img	29.050003	Imaginary part of antilogarithm

2nd Abs—Absolute Value Key

2nd Abs calculates the absolute value of the real or complex number in the display. The absolute value of a number is the magnitude of the number regardless of the sign. Thus the result of 2nd Abs is always a positive number. Pressing EXC θ after pressing 2nd Abs shows a 0 in the display. The absolute value of a polar number is the magnitude of r with a zero angle. The absolute value function does not affect a pending operation.

x:y—X Exchange Y Key

In the complex number mode, the x:y key is not a data entry key. It is an operation key and can be used to swap the divisor and dividend in division, x and y in y^x, and $^x\sqrt{y}$, etc. When pressed in the complex number mode, the x:y key exchanges the complex number entered after the operation key with the complex number entered before the operation key. The parts are swapped real for real and imaginary for imaginary.

Example: Calculate $(2 + 3i) \div (4 + 5i) =$ using the $\boxed{x:y}$ key to swap the divisor and dividend

Press	Display	Comments
$\boxed{\text{ON/C}}$ $\boxed{\text{ON/C}}$	0	Clear display and pending operations
5 $\boxed{\text{Img}}$ 4	4	Enter the divisor
$\boxed{\div}$	4	Enter $\boxed{\div}$ operation
3 $\boxed{\text{Img}}$ 2	2	Enter the dividend
$\boxed{x:y}$	4	$\boxed{x:y}$ key swaps the divisor and dividend
$\boxed{=}$	0.5609756	Division completed with real part of the result in the display
$\boxed{\text{EXC}}$ $\boxed{\text{Img}}$	0.0487805	Display imaginary part of result

The following list shows how the functions operate in the complex number mode.

● Functions Valid in the Complex Number Mode

Completes Pending operation
$\boxed{+}$, $\boxed{-}$, $\boxed{\div}$, $\boxed{X}$, $\boxed{y^x}$, $\boxed{\text{INV}}$ $\boxed{y^x}$, $\boxed{=}$

Does not Complete Pending Operation
$\boxed{1/x}$, $\boxed{x^2}$, $\boxed{\sqrt{x}}$, $\boxed{\log}$, $\boxed{\ln x}$, $\boxed{\text{INV}}$ $\boxed{\log}$, $\boxed{\text{INV}}$ $\boxed{\ln x}$, $\boxed{\text{2nd}}$ $\boxed{\text{Abs}}$, $\boxed{\text{2nd}}$
$\boxed{\text{Fix}}$, $\boxed{\text{DRG}}$, $\boxed{\text{2nd}}$ $\boxed{\text{DRG►}}$, $\boxed{\text{EE}}$, $\boxed{\text{INV}}$ $\boxed{\text{EE}}$, $\boxed{\text{2nd}}$ $\boxed{\text{Eng}}$, $\boxed{\text{2nd}}$ $\boxed{\text{INV}}$ $\boxed{\text{Eng}}$,
$\boxed{\text{2nd}}$ $\boxed{\text{P↔R}}$, $\boxed{\text{INV}}$ $\boxed{\text{2nd}}$ $\boxed{\text{P↔R}}$, $\boxed{\text{2nd}}$ $\boxed{\text{DMS-DD}}$, $\boxed{x:y}$

● Functions Not Valid in the Complex Number Mode

Ignored Operations
$\boxed{\sin}$, $\boxed{\cos}$, $\boxed{\tan}$, $\boxed{\text{hyp}}$, $\boxed{\text{2nd}}$ $\boxed{\text{Intg}}$, $\boxed{\text{2nd}}$ $\boxed{\text{Frac}}$, $\boxed{\text{2nd}}$ $\boxed{x!}$, $\boxed{\text{2nd}}$ $\boxed{\text{nPr}}$,
$\boxed{\text{2nd}}$ $\boxed{\text{nCr}}$, $\boxed{\%}$, $\boxed{\text{2nd}}$ $\boxed{\Delta\%}$, all STAT keys

Error Producing
$\boxed{K}$, $\boxed{(}$, $\boxed{)}$

Wait for CALC to disappear from the display before making more entries. Entries made while CALC is in the display are ignored, which may result in a wrong answer.

SECTION 5—COMPLEX NUMBER KEYS

Note that doing x², log, lnx, y^x, and their inverses in succession (for example, $\boxed{x^2}$, $\boxed{x^2}$, $\boxed{x^2}$, $\boxed{\sqrt{x}}$, $\boxed{\sqrt{x}}$, $\boxed{\sqrt{x}}$) may or may not produce the same answer. This is due to the fact that these functions use rectangular to polar conversions internally and all such calculations use the principal value of the argument. In other words the range is $-\pi < \theta \leq \pi$ radians.

CONVERSIONS

Angular measurement conversions, polar/rectangular conversions, and decimal degrees to degrees/minutes/seconds conversions can be carried out while in the complex number mode.

$\boxed{\text{DRG}}$, $\boxed{\text{2nd}}$ $\boxed{\text{DRG►}}$—Degree/Radian/Grad Conversions

The calculator is always in degree mode when it is turned on indicated by the absence of both RAD and GRAD in the display. Pressing $\boxed{\text{DRG}}$ changes it to radian mode, indicated by RAD in the display. Pressing $\boxed{\text{DRG}}$ again changes it to grad mode, indicated by GRAD in the display. Pressing $\boxed{\text{DRG}}$ again returns the calculator to degree mode. You may also go through the modes in reverse order—from degrees to grads to radians and back to degrees—by pressing the $\boxed{\text{INV}}$ $\boxed{\text{DRG}}$ key.

The $\boxed{\text{2nd}}$ $\boxed{\text{DRG►}}$ key also changes the mode displayed, and additionally converts the number in the *display* to the new units. Thus 90 in the degree mode followed by $\boxed{\text{2nd}}$ $\boxed{\text{DRG►}}$ changes the mode to radians and the display to 1.5707963 ($\pi/2$). Pressing $\boxed{\text{2nd}}$ $\boxed{\text{DRG►}}$ again changes the mode to grads and the display to 100. You may also go through the modes and values in reverse order—from degrees to grads to radians and back to degrees—by pressing the $\boxed{\text{INV}}$ $\boxed{\text{2nd}}$ $\boxed{\text{DRG►}}$ key.

Important: The $\boxed{\text{2nd}}$ $\boxed{\text{DRG►}}$ key works only on the displayed value. The other part if previously entered is not affected. Therefore, you must be sure to press it after entering the θ value and before pressing the $\boxed{\theta}$ key if conversion of the θ value is desired. Pressing $\boxed{\text{2nd}}$ $\boxed{\text{DRG►}}$ right after entering the r value converts the r value and the θ value remains unchanged.

Example: Enter 5 /32.2° and convert the angle to radians, then grads, and back to degrees.

Press DRG until neither RAD or GRAD is in the display. This ensures that the calculator is in the degree mode.

Press	Display	Comments
ON/c ON/c	0	Clear display and pending operations
32.2 [2nd] DRG►	0.561996	Angle is converted to radians as indicated by RAD in the display
[2nd] DRG►	35.777778	Angle is converted to grads as indicated by GRAD in the display
[2nd] DRG►	32.2	Angle is converted to degrees as indicated by the absence of both RAD and GRAD from the display
θ	0	Enter angle as θ value
5	5	Enter r value
EXC θ	32.2	Display θ value
EXC θ	5	Return r value to the display

[2nd] DMS-DD—Decimal Degrees to Degrees/Minutes/Seconds Conversions

The calculator also converts from decimal degrees to degrees/minutes/seconds and vice versa while in the complex number mode. Like the [2nd] DRG► key, the [2nd] DMS-DD key operates on the displayed value only. So be sure to press it after entering the θ value and before pressing the θ key if conversion of the θ value is desired. Pressing the [2nd] DMS-DD key after entering the r value, converts the r value and the θ value remains unchanged.

SECTION 5—COMPLEX NUMBER KEYS

[2nd] [P↔R], [INV] [2nd] [P↔R]—Polar/Rectangular Conversions

The calculator can perform polar/rectangular conversions while in the complex number mode.

To convert from polar form to rectangular form, follow these steps:

- Enter the θ value
- Press [θ]
- Enter the r value
- Press [2nd] [P↔R]

The real value is displayed.

- Press [EXC] [Img]

The imaginary value is displayed.

Note that the entry of values for polar/rectangular conversions in the complex number mode is the opposite order of the entry of paired values in the other modes. Remember that complex numbers entered in polar form are automatically converted to rectangular form any time an operation is pressed. If the complex number is already in rectangular form when the [2nd] [P↔R] key is pressed, the operation is ignored.

To convert from rectangular form to polar form follow these steps:

- Enter the imaginary part of the complex number
- Press [Img]
- Enter the real part of the complex number
- Press [INV] [2nd] [P↔R]

The r value is displayed.

- Press [EXC] [θ]

The θ value is displayed in the units selected by the [DRG] key.

Both the CMPLX and r,θ indicators are shown. The r,θ indicator is seen anytime the complex number is in polar form. If the complex number is already in polar form when the [INV] [2nd] [P↔R] key is pressed, the operation is ignored.

All the rectangular to polar conversions have an infinite number of values for the argument. However, the calculator always uses the principal value for θ, that is, $-\pi < \theta \leq \pi$ radians. Other values for θ can be obtained by adding $\pm 2n\pi$ radians to it where n = 0, 1, . . ., ∞. When converting the rectangular value (0,0) to polar, the θ value has arbitrarily been chosen as 90°, or $\pi/2$ radians, or 100 grads.

Example: Convert (5 + 3i) to polar form.

Be sure that the angular mode setting is the desired one. The θ value is displayed in the units selected by the DRG key.

Press DRG until neither RAD or GRAD is seen in the display. This ensures that the calculator is in the degree mode.

Press	Display	Comments
ON/C ON/C	0	Clear display and pending operations
3	3	Enter imaginary part
Img	0	
5	5	Enter real part of complex number
INV 2nd P→R	5.8309519	Complex number is converted to polar form as indicated by the r,θ indicator in the display. The value in the display is the r value
EXC θ	30.963757	Display θ value. CMPLX indicator blinks
EXC θ	5.8309519	Return r value to the display

MEMORY OPERATIONS

The calculator has three pairs of user data memories available for use in the complex number mode. When a complex number is stored in a user data memory, the real part is stored in one memory and the imaginary part is stored in a memory which has been paired to it. When you leave the complex number mode, only the *imaginary part* is cleared. The real values remain in the user data memories in which they were stored. The following keys allow manipulation of the values in the paired user data memories. Note that the memory arithmetic feature of the calculator does not operate in the complex number mode. Following a memory operation key with the functions $+$, $-$, $\times$, $\div$, y^x, or INV y^x, will produce an error message.

SECTION 5—COMPLEX NUMBER KEYS

[2nd] [CM]—Clear Memories Key

The [2nd] [CM] key clears the three paired user data memories available for use in the complex number mode. Both the real and the imaginary parts stored in memory are cleared.

[STO] m—Store Memories Key

The [STO] key is used to store values in the user data memories. To store a value, enter the complex number in rectangular or polar form, press [STO] and the number m (m = 0, 1, or 2) of the paired user data memory in which the value is to be stored. A complex number entered in polar form is converted to rectangular form when the [STO] key is pressed and then stored in the rectangular form. Before storing complex numbers entered in polar form, be sure to select the proper angular mode with the [DRG] key.

[RCL] m—Recall Memories Key

The [RCL] key.is used to recall the complex number stored in a paired user data memory m. The value recalled is always in rectangular form. To recall a number from memory, press [RCL] and the number m (m = 0, 1, or 2) of the paired user data memory to be displayed. The real part is displayed. To display the imaginary part, press [EXC] [Img].

[EXC] m—Exchange Memories Key

The [EXC] key is used to exchange a complex number whose real or r value is in the display with the complex number in the paired user data memory indicated. If the displayed complex number is in polar form, it is converted to rectangular form first and then the numbers are swapped real for real and imaginary for imaginary. Enter the complex number in rectangular or polar form, press [EXC] and the number of the paired user data memory to be exchanged. The value in the display is now the real part of the number that was stored in the memory addressed. To display the imaginary part, press [EXC] [Img].

Example: Store 3 + 5i in memory 0 and 3 /π÷3 in memory 1. Recall memory 0. Exchange the complex number recalled with the complex number stored in memory 1.

Press DRG until RAD is seen in the display. This indicates that the calculator is in the radian mode.

Press	Display	Comments
ON/c ON/c	0	Clear display and pending operations
5 Img 3 STO 0	3	Store 3 + 5i in memory 0
π ÷ 3 = θ 3	3	Enter complex number in polar form
STO 1*	1.5	When STO 1 is pressed, the complex number is converted to rectangular form and stored in memory 1
RCL 0	3	Recall the complex number in memory 0. The value in the display is the real part of the number
EXC Img	5	Display imaginary part of recalled number
EXC Img	3	Return real part of recalled number to the display
EXC 1	1.5	Exchange the complex number whose real part is in the display (3 + 5i), with the complex number stored in user data memory 1
EXC Img	2.5980762	Display imaginary part of exchanged number
EXC Img	1.5	Real part of exchanged number in display again

*Wait until CALC is removed from the display before doing the next operation. Entries made while CALC is in the display are ignored, which may result in a wrong answer.

Section 6—Statistical Keys

In many situations in business and everyday life, you may find yourself handling a set of data points. This data may be test scores, sales figures, weights of an incoming shipment, etc. The most common statistical calculations used to understand the meaning of that data are the mean and standard deviation. The mean (or average) value is the central tendency of the data. The standard deviation shows how variable the data are—how far the data tend to differ from the mean.

The calculator has special features that allow you to enter data quickly and calculate the mean and standard deviation. Here is the procedure:

- If CMPLX is in the display, press `INV` `Img` to take the calculator out of the complex number mode.
- Begin any statistical calculations with `ON/C` `ON/C` `2nd` `CSR`, to clear the display, pending operations, and the statistical registers.
- Enter each data point, then press the `Σ+` key. If you make a mistake, remove the data point by rekeying the error and pressing `2nd` `Σ−`. (Refer to the table at the end of this Section.) To enter the same data point up to 99 times, use the `2nd` `Frq` key. You may enter a total of up to 99,999 data points. Note: As you enter the data, the calculator displays the number of data points that have been entered.

When all data points are entered:

- Press `2nd` `Mean` to display the mean value of the data.
- Press `2nd` `σn-1` or `2nd` `σn` to calculate the standard deviation for the data. The `2nd` `σn-1` key is used when a sample taken from the population has been entered. The `2nd` `σn` key is used when the entire population has been entered.

STANDARD DEVIATION

For convenience, the option has been provided to select n weighting (with the `2nd` `σn` key) or n-1 weighting (with the `2nd` `σn-1` key) when finding the standard deviation. The `2nd` `σn` key results in a maximum likelihood estimator that is generally used to describe populations, while the `2nd` `σn-1` key is an unbiased estimator customarily used for sampled data.

SECTION 6—STATISTICAL KEYS

LINEAR REGRESSION

Linear regression provides a way to deal with one of the oldest problems in the world; predicting the future. With the linear regression keys on the calculator you can use data about past performances or relations to make forecasts of future performance (assuming that whatever relationship is at work continues). In this Section, the basic linear regression functions are shown with step-by-step procedures. Chapter 6 explains in detail how to use the linear regression keys.

Later chapters give examples illustrating how to use these keys in everyday, scientific, and business applications. It is not necessary to have a detailed background in statistics to use the tools the calculator provides. If you would like a brief review of some of the theory behind these keys, see Chapter 9.

In linear regression, data is usually expressed as pairs of variables that could be plotted on a graph. The points are usually labeled with the letters (x,y). "x" may be dollars spent for advertising while "y" is sales, or "x" may be a test score and "y" a performance record, etc. You want to make a prediction: For any given "x" value, what is the predicted value of "y", and vice versa? The calculator determines the best straight line through the data points. You may then use the straight line to make predictions. Here are the steps to do this:

- If CMPLX is in the display, press [INV] [Img]. This takes the calculator out of the complex number mode.
- Begin linear regression calculations with [ON/c] [ON/c] [2nd] [CSR], to clear the display, pending operations, and the statistical registers.
- Enter an "x" value and press [x:y].
- Enter the corresponding "y" value and press [Σ+].
- The [2nd] [Frq] key can be used to enter duplicate "x" and "y" values just as in statistics problems. Refer to the table at the end of this section.
- Continue until all data points are entered.

The calculator is now ready to draw the best straight line through the points and give the slope and intercept, and to predict an "x" for a "y" you enter or a "y" for an "x" you enter.

See the note after the explanation of 2nd **y'** and 2nd **x'**.

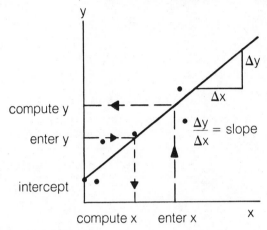

TREND LINE ANALYSIS

Trend line calculations are the same as linear regression calculations except that the "x" values increment by one for each "y" value entered. You may enter the first value; otherwise a value of 0 is used as a starting point for the "x" values if ON/c ON/c is pressed before starting the trend line analysis entry. The calculator automatically increments the "x" values by 1 as "y" values are entered.

The 2nd **Σ—** key does not decrement the "x" value, so errors in entry require reentry of all data.

THE STATISTICS KEYS

NOTE: Statistical functions use 5 of the calculator's memories, numbers 2 through 6. They are automatically cleared when the statistics mode is entered with `Σ+` or `2nd` `Frq`. To leave the statistics mode, press the `2nd` `CSR` key.

`2nd` `CSR`—Clear Statistical Registers Key

To return the calculator to normal calculation mode from statistics mode, press the `2nd` `CSR` key. The STAT indicator in the display is removed, indicating memories 2 through 6 are cleared.

`Σ+`, `2nd` `Σ−`, `2nd` `Frq`—Statistics Data Entry Keys

These keys are used to enter data points in statistics, linear regression, and trend line analysis calculations. The first time the `Σ+` or `2nd` `Frq` key is used, the calculator enters the statistics mode, displays STAT, and clears memories 2 through 6. The `Σ+` and `x:y` `Σ+` keys are used to enter data points, and the `2nd` `Σ−` and `x:y` `2nd` `Σ−` keys are used to remove data points. Note that the `Σ+` and `2nd` `Frq` keys clear any pending operations.

When several identical data points are to be entered, enter them with the `2nd` `Frq` ff `Σ+` and `x:y` `2nd` `Frq` ff `Σ+` keys, and remove them with the `2nd` `Frq` ff `2nd` `Σ−` and `x:y` `2nd` `Frq` ff `2nd` `Σ−` keys where ff may be from 1 to 99.

`2nd` `Mean`—Mean Keys

The `2nd` `Mean` key gives the mean of the "y" values entered. Then pressing `x:y` gives the mean of the "x" values entered. Note that the `2nd` `Mean` key removes any pending operations.

`2nd` `σn-1`, `2nd` `σn`—Standard Deviation Keys

The `2nd` `σn-1` and `2nd` `σn` keys give the sample and population standard deviation of the y data points that have been entered. The `2nd` `σn-1` `x:y` and `2nd` `σn` `x:y` keys give the sample and population standard deviation of the x data points that have been entered.

SECTION 6—STATISTICAL KEYS

The difference between the sample standard deviation ([2nd] [σn-1] and [2nd] [σn-1] [x̄:ȳ]) and the population standard deviation ([2nd] [σn] and [2nd] [σn] [x̄:ȳ]) becomes very small for over 30 data points. A population is usually a large set of items, and a sample is a smaller portion selected from the population. There is more about these terms in later chapters of the book. Note that the [2nd] [σn-1], [2nd] [σn], [2nd] [σn-1] [x̄:ȳ], and [2nd] [σn] [x̄:ȳ] keys remove any pending operations.

[2nd] [Corr]—Correlation Key

The [2nd] [Corr] key gives the correlation between the "x" and "y" values. A value near 1 indicates that the values are very closely related. A value near 0 indicates that the values are only slightly related. A value near −1 indicates that the values are very closely related, but in a negative way, that is, an increase in one is related to a decrease in the other.

[2nd] [b/a]—Intercept and Slope Keys

The [2nd] [b/a] key displays the intercept of the line the calculator determined was the best line through the points entered. Pressing the [x̄:ȳ] key then displays the slope of the line. Note that the [2nd] [b/a] and [2nd] [b/a] [x̄:ȳ] remove any pending operations.

[2nd] [y'], [2nd] [x']—Predicted Value Keys

After entering an "x" value, pressing the [2nd] [y'] key displays the "y" value that corresponds with that "x" on the line that the calculator determined was the best line through the points. Similarly, following a "y" value with [2nd] [x'] gives the corresponding "x'" value.

NOTE: Caution should be used in computing an "x'" (independent) value on the basis of a "y" (dependent) value. Further, it is not statistically valid to compute a "y'" value on the basis of an "x" which is outside the range of the entered "x" values. The predictions which result do not have statistical validity, and the probability figures that are found are not valid. However, trend line analysis and forecasting calculations often use these computations to make predictions or estimations of probability about the future. When performing such calculations, the actual values may differ from the calculated values.

STATISTICS EXAMPLES

Example: You are teaching a course and the first set of test scores is as shown below.

96	65	81	85	76	86	57	98
75	78	100	72	81	70	80	

What are the mean and standard deviation of these scores?

Enter all the scores with the $\boxed{\Sigma+}$ key. Then find the means and standard deviation with the $\boxed{2nd}$ Mean and $\boxed{2nd}$ On keys.

Press	Display	Comments
ON/c ON/c 2nd CSR	0	Clear display and pending operations. If necessary, clear statistics registers
96 $\boxed{\Sigma+}$	1	The STAT indicator appears in the display
65 $\boxed{\Sigma+}$	2	The calculator counts the data points
81 $\boxed{\Sigma+}$ 85 $\boxed{\Sigma+}$	4	
76 $\boxed{\Sigma+}$ 86 $\boxed{\Sigma+}$	6	
57 $\boxed{\Sigma+}$ 98 $\boxed{\Sigma+}$	8	
75 $\boxed{\Sigma+}$ 78 $\boxed{\Sigma+}$	10	
100 $\boxed{\Sigma+}$ 72 $\boxed{\Sigma+}$	12	
81 $\boxed{\Sigma+}$ 70 $\boxed{\Sigma+}$	14	
80 $\boxed{\Sigma+}$	15	
2nd Mean	80	Class average
2nd On	11.564313	Standard deviation

SECTION 6—STATISTICAL KEYS

Example: Suppose you have received a shipment of cans that are supposed to contain 4 liters of paint each. The volumes of a sample selected from the shipment are as follows.

1 can with a volume of 3.7 liters.
3 cans with a volume of 3.8 liters.
5 cans with a volume of 3.9 liters.
9 cans with a volume of 4.0 liters.
8 cans with a volume of 4.1 liters.
3 cans with a volume of 4.2 liters.
1 can with a volume of 4.3 liters.

What is the mean and standard deviation?

All 30 volumes could be entered using the [Σ+] key, but it is faster to use the [2nd] [Frq] key.

Press	Display	Comments
[ON/C] [ON/C] [2nd] [CSR]	0	Clear display, pending operations, and statistical registers
3.7 [Σ+]	1	Enter first value. STAT appears in the display
3.8 [2nd] [Frq]	Fr 00	Enter second value and frequency mode
3	Fr 03	Enter frequency value
[Σ+]	4	Number of values entered
3.9 [2nd] [Frq] 5 [Σ+]	9	Continue entry until all
4 [2nd] [Frq] 9 [Σ+]	18	points have been entered
4.1 [2nd] [Frq] 9 [Σ+]	27	Incorrect frequency entered
4.1 [2nd] [Σ−]	26	Incorrect value removed
4.2 [2nd] [Frq] 3 [Σ+]	29	
4.3 [Σ+]	30	
[2nd] [Mean]	4.01	Average volume
[2nd] [σn-1]	0.1373392	Standard deviation

Example: Suppose that you have been keeping records of the amount of rainfall each July in your city for the last five years. Can you use this data to predict the amount of rainfall this July? The data you have are shown below.

Year	Rainfall in centimeters
1976	8.6
1977	11.2
1978	11.0
1979	4.1
1980	5.3

Press	Display	Comments
ON/c ON/c 2nd CSR	0	Clear display, pending operations, and statistical registers
1976 x:y 8.6 Σ+	1	Enter first year and rainfall
11.2 Σ+	2	The x value is automatically incremented by one, to 1977
11 Σ+ 4.1 Σ+	4	
5.3 Σ+	5	
2nd Corr	−0.6677606	The correlation shows that rainfall per year is decreasing. -0.67 is not a very significant correlation
1981 2nd y'	3.9299999	The predicted rainfall

SECTION 6—STATISTICAL KEYS

PROCEDURES TO ENTER AND OBTAIN STATISTICAL DATA

The procedures to enter and remove an array of data are shown in the following chart.

SINGLE-VARIABLE DATA	TWO-VARIABLE DATA
1. To Enter Single Occurrence Data Points	
• Enter data point • Press $\boxed{\Sigma+}$ • Repeat for next data point	• Enter "x" data point • Press $\boxed{x:y}$ • Enter "y" data point • Press $\boxed{\Sigma+}$ • Repeat for next data point
2. To Remove Single Occurrence Data Points Entered	
• Press $\boxed{ON/c}$ $\boxed{x:y}$ • Enter unwanted data point • Press $\boxed{2nd}$ $\boxed{\Sigma-}$	• Enter unwanted "x" data point • Press $\boxed{x:y}$ • Enter unwanted "y" data point • Press $\boxed{2nd}$ $\boxed{\Sigma-}$
3. To Enter Multiple Occurrence Data Points	
• Enter data point • Press $\boxed{2nd}$ $\boxed{Frq}$ • Enter number of repetitions • Press $\boxed{\Sigma+}$ • Repeat for next data points	• Enter "x" data point • Press $\boxed{x:y}$ • Enter "y" data point • Press $\boxed{2nd}$ $\boxed{Frq}$ • Enter number of repetitions • Press $\boxed{\Sigma+}$ • Repeat for next data points
4. To Remove Multiple Occurrence Data Points Entered	
• Press $\boxed{ON/c}$ $\boxed{x:y}$ • Enter unwanted data point • Press $\boxed{2nd}$ $\boxed{Frq}$ • Enter number of repetitions • Press $\boxed{2nd}$ $\boxed{\Sigma-}$	• Enter unwanted "x" data point • Press $\boxed{x:y}$ • Enter unwanted "y" data point • Press $\boxed{2nd}$ $\boxed{Frq}$ • Enter number of repetitions • Press $\boxed{2nd}$ $\boxed{\Sigma-}$

The procedures to obtain data are shown in the following chart.

SINGLE VARIABLE DATA	TWO-VARIABLE DATA
1. Mean	
● Press [2nd] [Mean]	● "y" data points: Press [2nd] [Mean] ● "x" data points: Press [2nd] [Mean] [x≈y]
2. Population Standard Deviation	
● Press [2nd] [σn]	● "y" data points: Press [2nd] [σn] ● "x" data points: Press [2nd] [σn] [x≈y]
3. Sample Standard Deviation	
● Press [2nd] [σn-1]	● "y" data points: Press [2nd] [σn-1] ● "x" data points: Press [2nd] [σn-1] [x≈y]
4. Intercept and Slope	

	● Press [2nd] [b/a] to obtain the
	  intercept
	● Press [2nd] [b/a] [x≈y] to obtain
	  the slope

5. One Value Given Another	

	● Enter the x value and press
	  [2nd] [y'] to obtain a "y" value
	● Enter the y value and press
	  [2nd] [x'] to obtain an "x" value

6. Correlation	
	● Press [2nd] [Corr]

Mathematical Applications

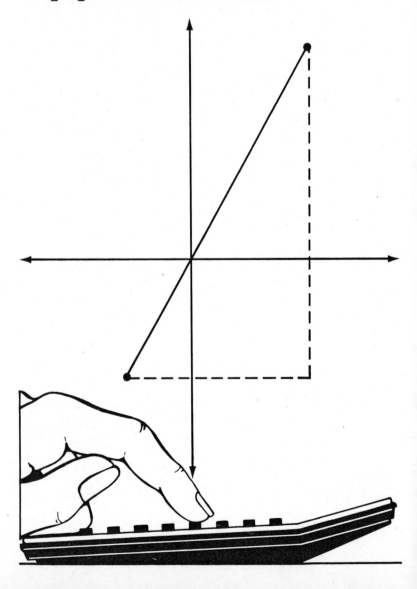

Mathematics can be fascinating and fun, but it can also turn into a tedious chore. Cumbersome numbers and repetitive calculations can obscure the interesting behavior of mathematical functions with errors and mistakes. However, with your calculator handling the arithmetic, you can concentrate on the concepts and techniques of mathematics. This chapter shows a few of the ways you can apply this scientific calculator to various situations.

Area of a Triangle

Suppose you are considering buying a triangular piece of property as an investment. The owner wants $50,000 for the plot, which is bounded on all three sides by unpaved roads, but he is not sure how much land there actually is. You plan to subdivide and sell the plot by the acre, so you need an estimate of the cost per acre to predict what your profits will be. Using the odometer in your car, you find the lengths of the three sides of the plot to be 0.3, 0.5, and 0.75 miles.

Target: You want to calculate the area of the property and the cost per acre.

Tools: The Heron formula can help solve this problem. This formula uses the lengths of the sides of the triangle to determine its area, and is written as

$$\text{Area} = \sqrt{S(S-a)(S-b)(S-c)}$$

where a, b, and c are the lengths of the sides and S is given by

$$S = \frac{1}{2}(a + b + c)$$

An acre of land is 43,600 square feet, and a square mile contains 5280^2 square feet. The conversion factor for square miles to acres is therefore

$$\frac{5280^2}{43600}$$

Keying it in:

Press	Display	Comments
ON/c ON/c INV 2nd Fix	0	Clear display and pending operations and reset to standard notation
.5 X (.3 + .5 + .75) = STO 0	0.8 0.775	Calculate the value of S and store it in memory 0.
X (RCL 0* − .3)	0.475	Calculate the area in square miles.
X (RCL 0 − .5) X	0.1012344	
(RCL 0 − .75) = √x	0.0503076	Area in square miles
X 5280 x² ÷	1402496.7	
43600 = ÷	32.167356	Convert area to acres.
50000 x:y =	1554.3708	To divide 50000 by the area, enter the division and then exchange the x and y values. Result is the cost per acre

*As mentioned in Chapter 1, the open parenthesis can repeat a displayed number. Thus RCL 0 could be omitted here to save two keystrokes.

Pythagorean Theorem

Frequently in mathematics a special kind of triangle called a right triangle is used. A right triangle is one which has a 90° angle.   Because these triangles have special conditions they also have special properties.

A Greek philosopher, Pythagoras (580-500 B.C.), developed the right triangle relation which was given his name. The Pythagorean theorem says that no matter how you draw a right triangle, the square of the longest side equals the sum of the squares of the other two sides. As a formula the Pythagorean Theorem is written $c^2 = a^2 + b^2$.

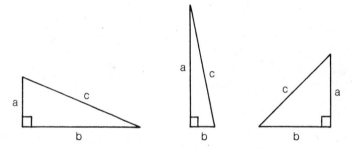

Because of this special property of right triangles, if the length of any two sides is known, the missing side is easily found. Suppose a radio antenna tower is 10 meters tall and is to be anchored by three guy wires placed six meters from the base.

MATHEMATICAL APPLICATIONS

PYTHAGOREAN THEOREM

Target: Determine the total amount of guy wire needed.

Tools: The tower makes a right angle with the ground, so the Pythagorean theorem can be used to solve for the missing side.

(length of guy wire)^2 = (height of tower)^2 + (distance along the ground)^2

(length of guy wire)^2 = $10^2 + 6^2$

length of guy wire = $\sqrt{10^2 + 6^2}$

Once the length of one guy wire is determined, multiply by three to determine the total amount needed.

Keying it in:

Press	Display	Comments
$\boxed{\text{ON/c}}$ $\boxed{\text{ON/c}}$	0	Clear display and pending operations
10 $\boxed{x^2}$ $\boxed{+}$	100	
6 $\boxed{x^2}$ $\boxed{=}$	136	
$\boxed{\sqrt{x}}$	11.661904	Length of one guy wire
$\boxed{\times}$ 3 $\boxed{=}$	34.985711	Total length of guy wires. You need to purchase at least 35 meters

Distance Formula

The Cartesian coordinate system consists of two perpendicular lines with the horizontal line called the x-axis and the vertical line called the y-axis. The two lines intersect at the point called the origin. The "x" values to the right of the y-axis are positive and to the left of the y-axis are negative. The "y" values above the x-axis are positive and below the x-axis are negative. Thus, any point P can be represented by an ordered pair of numbers, (x,y), such that "x" is the distance from the y-axis and "y" is the distance from the x-axis. These are called the rectangular coordinates of the point P.

 Target: Find the distance between the points $(-3,-6)$ and $(4,9)$.

Tools: Rearranging the Pythagorean theorem gives an easy method of calculating the distance between any two points (x_1,y_1) and (x_2,y_2) on a graph.

$$\text{Distance} = \sqrt{(x_2 - x_1)^2 + (y_2 - y_1)^2}$$

For this example:

$$\text{Distance} = \sqrt{(4 - (-3))^2 + (9 - (-6))^2}$$

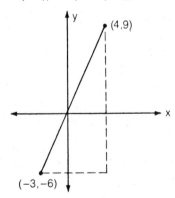

DISTANCE FORMULA

Keying it in:

Press	Display	Comments
ON/C ON/C	0	Clear display and pending operations
(4 − 3 +/−)	7	Enter x coordinates
x^2	49	Square x coordinates
+ (9 − 6 +/−)	15	Enter y coordinates
x^2	225	Square y coordinates
=	274	Sum squares of x and y coordinates
$\sqrt{x}$	16.552945	The points are about 16.6 units apart

Polar/Rectangular Conversions

The polar coordinate system consists of a point called the origin and a fixed ray radiating horizontally from the origin. Any point in the polar coordinate system may be represented by the ordered pair of numbers (r,θ) such that r is the distance from the origin to the point and θ is the angle measured from the fixed ray to the line which joins the origin and the point. θ is positive if measured counter-clockwise and negative if measured clockwise.

Points which are represented as rectangular coordinates can be converted to polar coordinates and vice versa. Your calculator has keys to convert from rectangular to polar and vice versa so that these two methods can be easily interchanged.

Example: A man starts at point A and travels two miles north-easterly at an angle of 30°. He then turns and travels east for five miles, turns again and travels southeasterly (−45°) for two miles, turns again and travels due south (−90°) for one mile, and completes his journey by traveling ten miles in a north-easterly (60°) direction to point B.

Target: Determine the angle for a straight trip from point A to point B and the length of a straight trip from point A to point B.

Tools: Change all the polar coordinates to rectangular coordinates and sum the x and y values. The angle from the horizontal and the distance traveled from A to B are then obtained by converting the sums back to polar coordinates.

MATHEMATICAL APPLICATIONS

POLAR/RECTANGULAR CONVERSIONS

The key sequences for the conversions are as follows:

Polar to Rectangular	Rectangular to Polar
Enter "r" coordinate	Enter "x" coordinate
Press $x{:}y$	Press $x{:}y$
Enter "θ" coordinate	Enter "y" coordinate
Press 2nd P→R	Press INV 2nd P→R
y value displayed	θ value displayed
Press $x{:}y$	Press $x{:}y$
x value displayed	r value displayed

Keying it in: In this solution the sum of the y coordinates is stored in memory 0 and the sum of the x coordinates is stored in memory 1. If RAD or GRAD is in the display, press DRG until neither shows. This ensures that the calculator is in the degree mode.

Press	Display	Comments
ON/C ON/C	0	Clear display and pending operations
2 $x{:}y$ 30 2nd P→R	1	Enter first pair of polar coordinates and convert to rectangular coordinates
STO 0	1	Store y-value in memory 0
$x{:}y$ STO 1	1.7320508	Store x-value in memory 1
5 $x{:}y$ 0 2nd P→R	0	Enter second pair of polar coordinates and convert to rectangular coordinates
STO + 0	0	Add new y-value to memory 0
$x{:}y$ STO + 1	5	Add new x-value to memory 1

(continued)

(continued)

Press	Display	Comments
2 [x:y] 45 [+/−] [2nd] [P→R]	−1.4142136	Enter third pair of polar coordinates and convert to rectangular coordinates
[STO] [+] 0	−1.4142136	Add new y-value
[x:y] [STO] [+] 1	1.4142136	Add new x-value
1 [x:y] 90 [+/−] [2nd] [P→R]	−1	Enter fourth pair of polar coordinates and convert to rectangular coordinates
[STO] [+] 0	−1	Add new y-value
[x:y] [STO] [+] 1	0	Add new x-value
10 [x:y] 60 [2nd] [P→R]	8.660254	Enter fifth pair of polar coordinates and convert to rectangular coordinates
[STO] [+] 0	8.660254	Add new y-value
[x:y] [STO] [+] 1	5	Add new x-value
[RCL] 1	13.146264	Recall total of x-values for conversions
[x:y] [RCL] 0	7.2460405	Recall total of y-values for conversions
[INV] [2nd] [P→R]	28.862951	Angle of line AB from the horizontal
[x:y]	15.010975	Distance from point A to point B

Law of Cosines

One of the plane triangle formulas frequently used is the Law of Cosines. The Law of Cosines states that if two sides and the included angle of a triangle are known, the third side can be determined.

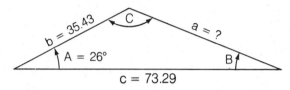

 Target: If the length of b is 35.43 centimeters, c is 73.29 centimeters and the angle A is 26°, find the length of a.

Tools: The Law of Cosines is written as:

$$a^2 = b^2 + c^2 - 2bc \cos A$$

The length of a is $\sqrt{b^2 + c^2 - 2bc \cos A}$

Keying it in: If RAD or GRAD is in the display, press $\boxed{\text{DRG}}$ until neither is shown. This indicates that the calculator is in the degree mode.

Press	Display	Comments
$\boxed{\text{ON/c}}$ $\boxed{\text{ON/c}}$	0	Clear display and pending operations
35.43 $\boxed{x^2}$	1255.2849	Length of first side squared
$\boxed{+}$ 73.29 $\boxed{x^2}$	5371.4241	Plus length of second side squared
$\boxed{-}$ 2 $\boxed{\times}$ 35.43	35.43	$- 2b$
$\boxed{\times}$ 73.29	73.29	Times c
$\boxed{\times}$ 26 $\boxed{\text{cos}}$	0.898794	Times the cosine of 26°
$\boxed{=}$	1958.9755	$b^2 + c^2 - 2bc \cos A$
$\boxed{\sqrt{x}}$ $\boxed{\text{STO}}$ 0	44.260315	Length of missing side. Store it in memory 0 so that it can be used in the next section

Going Further: Now that the lengths of the three sides are known what are angles B and C? The Law of Cosines can once again be used to solve for angle B.

The Law of Cosines can be rewritten as

$$b^2 = a^2 + c^2 - 2ac \cos B.$$

or

$$B = \arccos \left(\frac{a^2 + c^2 - b^2}{2ac} \right)$$

After B is found, subtract angles A and B from 180° to find angle C since the sum of the angles of a triangle always equals 180°.

Keying it in: If RAD or GRAD is in the display, press DRG until neither is shown. This indicates that the calculator is in the degree mode. Memory 0 contains the result from the previous example even if the calculator has been turned off.

Press	Display	Comments
(x^2	1958.9755	Square the length of a. If the calculator has been turned off or cleared, this value must be recalled from memory 0
+ 73.29 x^2	5371.4241	Add the length of c squared
− 35.43 x^2)	6075.1147	Subtract the length of b squared
÷ (2 ×	2	Divide by 2 times ac
RCL 0 × 73.29	73.29	
=	0.9364083	Result
INV cos STO 1	20.543127	Arccosine gives angle B. Store this value in memory 1
180 − 26 −	154	Subtract the two known angles from 180°
RCL 1 =	133.45687	Angle C

Hyperbolic Functions

The shape that an ideally flexible wire makes when hanging between two points is called a catenary. Mathematicians have determined various formulas concerning catenaries which involve hyperbolic trigonometric functions. Suppose a wire is suspended from two poles 150 feet apart from two pegs at the same level and dips 25 feet at its lowest point. The wire weighs .1 pound/foot. The horizontal tension on the wire at the lowest point is 11.6 pounds.

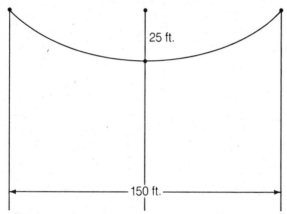

25 ft.

150 ft.

Target: Determine the length of the wire.

Tools: Half the length of the wire is given by the following formula

$$s = \frac{H}{w} \times \sinh \frac{wx}{H}$$

where
    H = the horizontal tension
    w = the weight of the wire in pounds per foot
    x = half the distance between the poles

Sinh indicates that the hyperbolic sine function is used. Angular mode has no effect on hyperbolic functions. Once half of the wire is determined, multiply by two to determine the length of the wire.

Keying It In:

Press	Display	Comments
ON/C ON/C	0	Clear display and pending operations
11.6 ÷ .1	0.1	Enter H/w
X (.1 X 75	75	Multiply w by x
÷ 11.6)	0.6465517	Divide by H
hyp sin	0.6925489	Calculate the hyperbolic sine of wx/H
=	80.335675	Length of half the wire
X 2 =	160.67135	Total length of the wire

Quadratic Equations

Equations are often encountered in scientific and engineering calculations that have the form $ax^2 + bx + c = 0$. Equations of this form are known as quadratic equations. Solving for x, or finding the roots of the equation, may be done by several methods. In some cases, you may be able to factor the equation into its basic components by inspection. Sometimes, however, factoring a quadratic equation can be difficult, or nearly impossible. For example, consider the quadratic equation:

$$2x^2 + 5x + 1 = 0$$

Target: Determine the roots of the quadratic equation $2x^2 + 5x + 1 = 0$.

Tools: In cases where factoring proves difficult, you may want to use the quadratic formula, which gives the roots of any quadratic equation. It is written as

$$x = \frac{-b \pm \sqrt{b^2 - 4ac}}{2a}$$

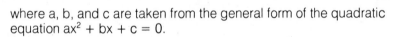

where a, b, and c are taken from the general form of the quadratic equation $ax^2 + bx + c = 0$.

Keying it in: The following example solves $\sqrt{b^2 - 4ac}$ first and stores the result in memory 0 to be recalled later in solving for the roots.

Press	Display	Comments
ON/C ON/C	0	Clear display and pending operations
5 x^2 −	25	b^2
4 X 2 X 1 =	17	b^2 - 4ac
$\sqrt{x}$ STO 0	4.1231056	$\sqrt{b^2 - 4ac}$ stored in memory 0
(5 +/−	−5	−b
+ RCL 0)	−0.8768944	Plus $\sqrt{b^2 - 4ac}$
÷ (2 X 2 =	−0.2192236	First root of equation
(5 +/−	−5	−b
− RCL 0)	−9.1231056	Minus $\sqrt{b^2 - 4ac}$
÷ (2 X 2 =	−2.2807764	Second root of equation

Scientific Applications

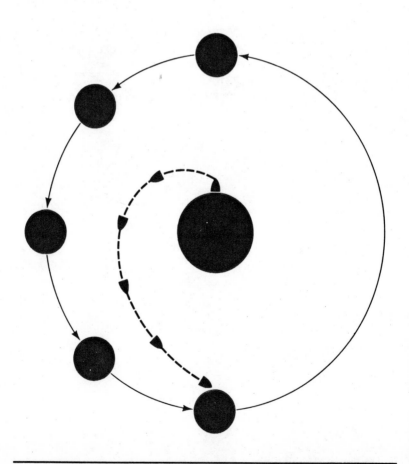

Mathematics, simple and complex, is used in applying scientific principles. The scientific principles involved may be fascinating but the tedious math may make it frustrating. Your calculator quickly and accurately handles the math allowing you to concentrate on the science. This chapter shows a few of the possible scientific applications.

Astronomical Numbers

Science frequently deals with very large and very small numbers. A simple way to write these numbers is in scientific notation. When a number is written in scientific notation, it is expressed as a base (the mantissa) times 10 raised to some power (the exponent). A negative mantissa indicates a negative number. A negative exponent indicates how many places the decimal point must be shifted to the left to display the number in standard notation. A positive exponent, on the other hand, indicates how many places the decimal point must be shifted to the right to display the number in standard notation.

Standard Notation	Scientific Notation
3500	3.5×10^3
1,000,000	1×10^6
.0025	2.5×10^{-3}
−456,123,000	-4.56123×10^8

The universe is so large that the light-year (the distance light travels in a year) is often used to describe it. Earth's nearest neighboring star (other than the sun) is approximately 4.3 light-years away.

Target: Determine the length of time it would take a car, at 55 miles per hour, to travel 4.3 light years.

Tools: Light travels at the rate of 2.9979×10^8 meters per second which equals 186,281 miles per second. To solve the problem all values must be in the same unit of measurement. For this example, it is easiest to convert both units to years to obtain the number of years traveled.

Keying it in: Note that the calculator continues to calculate values in scientific notation until it is cancelled by pressing [INV] [EE], [ON/c], or turning the calculator off and back on.

Press	Display	Comments
[ON/c] [ON/c]	0	Clear display and pending operations
[( ] 1.86281 [EE] 5 [X] 60	60	
[X] 60 [X] 24 [X] 365.25	365.25	
[X] 4.3 [ )] [÷] [( ] 55 [X] 24 [X]	2.52779 13	4.3 light-years in miles
365.25 [ )]	4.8213 05	Miles traveled in one year at 55 miles per hour
[=]	5.2429634 07	Years needed to travel 4.3 light-years displayed in scientific notation
[INV] [EE]	52429634	Result in standard notation

Do not clear or turn off the calculator. The previous result is used in the next example.

Going further: Astronauts going to the moon have traveled at about 25,000 miles per hour. That's much faster than the 55 mile per hour speed limit but even at this speed it takes a long time to reach the next star.

Using the value already in the display from the previous calculation, multiply by 55 miles per hour and divide by 25,000 miles per hour. The result is the time in years it takes to travel 4.3 light-years at a speed of 25,000 miles per hour.

Keying it in:

Press	Display	Comments
⟨X⟩ 55 ⟨÷⟩ 2.5 ⟨EE⟩ 4		
⟨=⟩	1.153452 05	Result in years displayed in scientific notation
⟨INV⟩ ⟨EE⟩	115345.2	Result in standard notation

Electrical Resistance and Ohm's Law

Appliances are plugged into wall outlets connected in parallel across the house supply voltage. George Simon Ohm (1787-1854), a German physicist, wrote a pamphlet on electric currents. The most important part is now called Ohm's Law. It states that E (the voltage in the outlet) = I (the total current that will flow measured in amperes) times R (the total resistance measured in ohms).

Five appliances with individual resistances of 5 ohms (Ω), 12 ohms, 17 ohms, 23 ohms, and 49 ohms respectively are plugged into house wall outlets. Assuming the house supply voltage is 115, an electrician would draw a diagram like the one below.

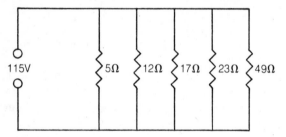

Target: Determine the current that the five appliances will draw if they are all turned on at the same time.

Tools: Solving for I (total current that will flow) in Ohm's Law obtains I = E÷R. Before using this formula, however, you need to determine R (the total resistance).

The law of parallel resistors states that $1 \div R_t = 1 \div R_1 + 1 \div R_2 + 1 \div R_3 + ...$ Substituting the known resistor values into this formula, gives the total resistance. When combined with Ohm's Law, the total current drawn may be obtained.

ELECTRICAL RESISTANCE AND OHM'S LAW

Keying it in:

Press	Display	Comments
ON/C ON/C	0	Clear display and pending operations
5 1/x +	0.2	
12 1/x +	0.2833333	
17 1/x +	0.3421569	
23 1/x +	0.3856351	
49 1/x =	0.4060433	Result is $1/R_t$
1/x STO 0	2.4627916	The reciprocal of $1/R_t$ gives the total resistance. It is then stored in memory 0
115 ÷ RCL 0 =	46.694978	Total current in amperes

Going further: Many people leave a light burning all
the time. Suppose a 100-watt bulb is being used. How
much would be saved in a year by switching to a 60-
watt bulb at the rate of 6 cents per kilowatt hour?

The cost for one hour is the bulb wattage divided by 1000 times
the cost per kilowatt hour. Then the cost per year is the cost for one
hour times the hours in a day times the days in a year.

Press	Display	Comments
ON/c ON/c	0	Clear display and pending operations
60 ÷ 1000 × .06 =	0.0036	Cost for one hour with 60 watt bulb
× 24 × 365.25 = STO 0	31.5576	Cost for year for 60 watt bulb stored in memory 0
100 ÷ 1000 × .06 =	0.006	Cost for one hour with 100 watt bulb
× 24 × 365.25 =	52.596	Cost for year for 100 watt bulb
− RCL 0 =	21.0384	Dollar amount saved in one year by switching to a 60-watt bulb

Vectors

Vectors have a wide variety of applications in practical physics and provide a way to visualize problems. Vectors are measurable quantities that have both magnitude and direction. A vector is shown in a diagram by a directed line segment whose direction represents the direction of the vector and whose length represents its magnitude. Without the vector diagram, the next example would be more difficult to understand.

You wish to fly a small airplane to a city that is 800 miles directly north of your home airfield. The weather service has advised you that the prevailing winds at your cruising altitude are from the west and average 50 miles per hour. Before you can file an accurate flight plan, you need to know what your groundspeed will be, how long the flight will last at your true airspeed (the speed of the airplane relative to the air) of 220 miles per hour, and in what direction, or heading, you should fly.

Target: Determine the effect of a 50 mile per hour crosswind on your flight.

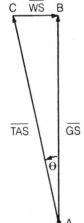

Tools: A good way to visualize this problem is to draw a vector diagram to scale, as shown. Vector AC illustrates the true airspeed ($\overline{TAS}$). Vector CB illustrates the crosswind speed ($\overline{WS}$), while vector AB shows the groundspeed vector ($\overline{GS}$). The angle θ is the heading angle taken to counteract the wind.

As you can see from the vector diagram, ABC is a right triangle, therefore, you can apply the Pythagorean theorem to solve for the groundspeed. The length of the flight is obtained by dividing the distance from the starting point to the airfield by the groundspeed. The heading angle in degrees is calculated by taking the arctangent of the result of the crosswind speed divided by the groundspeed.

Keying it in: After calculation, the groundspeed is stored in the first user data memory to be used in subsequent calculations.

If RAD or GRAD is in the display, press DRG until neither is shown. This indicates that the calculator is in the degree mode.

Press	Display	Comments
ON/C ON/C	0	Clear display and pending operations
220 x^2 —	48400	True airspeed squared
50 x^2	2500	Subtract crosswind speed squared
= $\sqrt{x}$ STO 0	214.24285	Groundspeed stored in memory 0
800 ÷	800	Distance to the airfield ·
RCL 0 =	3.7340802	Divided by groundspeed gives flight time in decimal hours
INV 2nd DMS-DD	3.4402689	Length of flight in hours/minutes/seconds — 3 hours 44 minutes 2.689 seconds
50 ÷	50	Crosswind speed
RCL 0 =	0.23338	Divided by groundspeed
INV tan	13.136559	Heading angle in degrees

Free Fall

Galileo Galilei (1564-1642) discovered in the 17th century that all objects fall with constant acceleration due to the force of gravity. The acceleration due to gravity is usually labeled with the letter g and is equal to 9.81 m/s^2, or 32.2 ft/s^2.

Target: Suppose a rock is thrown into a well 214 meters deep (d) at an initial velocity of 4 m/s (V_o). Determine how much time will pass before the rock hits the bottom of the well.

Tools: The formula for distance fallen is $d = 1/2gt^2 + V_ot$ where g is the gravitational constant, t is the time, and V_o is the starting velocity. This formula may be written as a quadratic equation $1/2gt^2 + V_ot - d = 0$. The quadratic equation for this example is $1/2(9.81)t^2 + 4t - 214 = 0$. Using the quadratic formula to solve for t gives

$t = (-b \pm \sqrt{b^2 - 4ac}) \div 2a$, where
$a = 1 \div 2 \times 9.81$ meters per second squared,
$b = 4$ meters per second, and
$c = -214$ meters.

Since time cannot be negative in this example, the positive root is the time it takes the rock to hit the bottom of the well.

Keying it in: In this example $\sqrt{b^2 - 4ac}$ is solved and stored in the first user data memory. Then 2a is solved and stored in the second user data memory. These two values are recalled to solve the quadratic equation.

Press	Display	Comments
ON/c ON/c	0	Clear display and pending operations
4 x^2 −	16	b^2
4 X .5 X 9.81	9.81	
X 214 +/− =	4214.68	Subtract 4ac
√x STO 0	64.920567	$\sqrt{b^2 - 4ac}$ stored in memory 0
2 X .5 X	1	
9.81 = STO 1	9.81	2a stored in memory 1
4 +/− + RCL 0 =	60.920567	
÷ RCL 1 =	6.2100476	First root of equation
4 +/− − RCL 0 =	−68.920567	
÷ RCL 1 =	−7.025542	Second root of equation

It takes approximately 6.2 seconds for the rock to hit the bottom of the well.

Projectiles

Experiments have shown that horizontal projectiles carry out two separate motions, a constant horizontal velocity due to the initial projection and a vertical velocity downward due to the acceleration from the force of gravity. By using vectors to sum these two velocities, the total velocity with which the projectile strikes the ground can be obtained. As an example, consider a stone thrown horizontally with a velocity of 40 feet per second from the top of a tower 100 feet high.

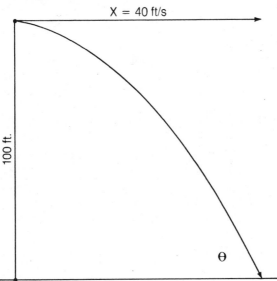

X = 40 ft/s

100 ft.

θ

 Target: Assuming no wind resistance, determine the velocity of the stone in feet per second when it strikes the ground.

Tools: The horizontal and vertical velocities must both be known before total velocity can be calculated. The horizontal velocity of the stone is given as 40 feet per second. To obtain the vertical velocity for the problem use the formula

$$\text{vertical velocity} = \sqrt{2gh}$$

where

g = 32.2 feet per second squared (the gravitational constant)
h = 100 feet (height of the tower)

After the vertical velocity has been obtained, enter the horizontal velocity (x) and the vertical velocity (y) and using the rectangular to polar conversion sequences calculate the angle the path of the stone makes with the ground (θ) and the total velocity with which the stone strikes the ground (r).

Keying It In: If RAD or GRAD is in the display, press DRG until neither is shown. This indicates that the calculator is in the degree mode.

Press	Display	Comments
ON/c ON/c	0	Clear display and pending operations
2 ✕ 100 ✕	200	Enter 2h
32.2 = √x	80.249611	Multiply by g and take the square root of 2gh. The result is the vertical velocity in ft/s
x:y	6440	Enter vertical velocity into x register
40 x:y	80.249611	Enter horizontal velocity in y register and exchange registers to put numbers in proper order
INV 2nd P→R	63.506279	Convert the horizontal and vertical velocities to polar coordinates. This is the angle that the projectile makes with the ground in degrees
x:y	89.666047	The total velocity with which the stone strikes the ground in ft/s

Moment of Inertia

Moment of inertia is the sum of all of the products of the mass of each particle in a rigid body and the square of its distance from an axis. The process of summing each of these moments of inertia is carried out by integration. Most of these integrations have been done and simple formulas are all that are needed to find the moment of inertia of many objects.

Consider the following situation: Two stones of 2 kilograms and 5 kilograms, respectively, are connected to opposite ends of a wire so that the centers of mass are 1.8 meters apart. This construction is then thrown into the air to rotate around their common center of mass.

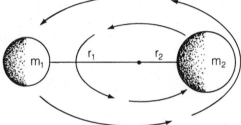

Target: Find the moment of inertia of the construction.

Tools: The solution to this problem requires several steps. The sum of the two radii must equal 1.8 meters.

$$r_1 + r_2 = 1.8$$
$$r_1 = 1.8 - r_2$$

Also for the common center of mass, the mass times the radius of one side must equal the mass times the radius of the other side.

$$m_1 r_1 = m_2 r_2$$

Substituting the value for r_1 obtained above yields

$$m_1(1.8 - r_2) = m_2 r_2$$
$$r_2 = 1.8 m_1 / (m_2 + m_1)$$

After obtaining r_2, substitute that value back into the equation $r_1 = 1.8 - r_2$ to get the other radius. Once both radii are known the moment of inertia is the sum of the two moments using the formula

Moment of inertia = $m_1 r_1{}^2 + m_2 r_2{}^2$

Keying It In: r_2 is stored in memory 0 after it has been calculated to avoid rekeying the number later in the solution.

Press	Display	Comments
ON/C ON/C	0	Clear display and pending operations
1.8 X 2	2	
÷ (5	5	
+ 2 = STO 0	0.5142857	Calculate r_2 and store in memory 0
+/− + 1.8 =	1.2857143	Calculate r_1
x^2 X 2 +	3.3061224	First moment of inertia
5 X	5	
RCL 0 x^2 =	4.6285714	Total moment of inertia in Kgm^2

Gas Laws

The motion of gas particles causes air to exert pressure. This pressure can be measured with a device called a barometer. Under normal conditions at sea level mercury in a barometer rises to a height of 760 millimeters. An atmosphere is defined to be the pressure sufficient to raise a column of mercury to a height of 760 millimeters (760 mm Hg). Atmospheres are frequently used as the measuring unit when dealing with gases. When applying gas laws, gas temperatures are measured in units of Kelvin degrees (K°). To the nearest whole number, the Kelvin temperature scale is simply the Celsius scale plus 273.

Suppose nitrogen gas is stored in a steel tank near a radiator. The pressure exerted by the nitrogen is 150 atmospheres at 77°F. Due to heating by the radiator the temperature of the nitrogen rises to 95°F.

Target: Determine the pressure exerted by the nitrogen at the higher temperature.

Tools: The volume of the steel tank is fixed as are the number of molecules of nitrogen in the tank. The only variables in this example are temperature and pressure. The gas law to use is $P_1/T_1 = P_2/T_2$. Solving for P_2 gives $P_2 = P_1 T_2/T_1$. Remember that the temperature scale used with gases is Kelvin. So first convert to Celsius and then add 273 to obtain the equivalent degrees on the Kelvin scale. The formula for conversion from Fahrenheit to Celsius is

$$°C = 5/9 \ (°F - 32).$$

Keying It In:

Press	Display	Comments
ON/C ON/C	0	Clear display and pending operations
150 ✕	150	Enter beginning pressure
(5 ÷ 9 ✕	0.5555556	Convert new temperature to Celsius
(95 − 32)	63	
+ 273)	308	Add 273 to convert to Kelvin
÷ (5 ÷ 9 ✕	0.5555556	Convert old temperature to Celsius
(77 − 32)	45	
+ 273)	298	Add 273 to convert to Kelvin
=	155.03356	New pressure exerted by the nitrogen in atmospheres

Radioactive Half-Life

The number of radioactive atoms left in a material after some time (t) in seconds is given by the disintegration formula $N_t = N_o e^{-kt}$ N_t is the number of atoms left after time t, N_o is the number of atoms in the original sample, e is the special number which is equal to 2.71828..., and k is the disintegration constant.

Half-life (T) is the time it takes for half the sample of radioactive material to disintegrate. Substituting $\frac{N_o}{2}$ for N_t and T for t in the formula above gives, $\frac{N_o}{2} = N_o e^{-kT}$. Solving this equation for T gives $.5 = e^{-kT}$. Taking the natural log of both sides gives $\ln(.5) = -kT$. Thus $T = \frac{\ln .5}{-k}$.

Target: Given that the disintegration constant (k) of radium is 1.36×10^{-11}/s, find its half-life.

Tools: To find half-life, use the disintegration constant in the formula derived above.

Keying it in:

Press	Display	Comments
[ON/C] [ON/C]	0	Clear display and pending operations
.5 [lnx] [÷]	−0.6931472	
1.36 [+/−] [EE] 11 [+/−]	−1.36−11	
[=]	5.0966704 10	Half-life in seconds displayed in scientific notation
[÷] 60 [÷] 60 [÷] 24	24	
[÷] 365.25 [=]	1.6150374 03	
[INV] [EE]	1615.0374	Half-life in years

Going further: What fraction of the radium remains after two years? To find the fraction of radium remaining use the formula $N_t = N_o e^{-kt}$. Dividing both sides by N_o, gives $\dfrac{N_t}{N_o} = e^{-kt}$ where t must be in seconds. Therefore, two years must be converted to seconds before using it in this formula.

Keying it in:

Press	Display	Comments
[ON/c] [ON/c]	0	Clear display and pending operations
2 [×] 365.25 [×] 24	24	
[×] 60 [×]	1051920	Calculate two years
60 [=]	63115200	in seconds
[×] 1.36 [+/−] [EE] 11		
[+/−]	−1.36−11	
[=] [INV] [lnx]	9.99142−01	The result displayed in scientific notation. Note that [INV] [lnx] is equal to e^x
[INV] [EE]	0.999142	Result in standard notation

Therefore 99.91% of the radium remains after 2 years.

Conduction

Some substances are better conductors of heat than others. The ability of a substance to conduct heat is its thermal conductivity. The thermal conductivity (k) is the number of kilocalories that pass from one face to the opposite face of a one meter cube in one second if the faces have a temperature difference of one degree Celsius. This is written mathematically as $k = \dfrac{Kcal/sq \; meter \; sec.}{C°/meter}$

A kilocalorie (Kcal) is the amount of heat required to raise one kilogram (Kg) of water one degree Celsius. If the thermal conductivity of an object is known, the amount of heat transfered through that object can be determined.

Target: A glass window pane is 1m by 1m and 5 mm thick. If snow outside the window maintains the outer surface at 0°C, and the heat from the room maintains the inner surface at 5°C, how much heat is conducted through the window in 24 hours?

Tools: The formula for the amount of heat conducted through an object is

$$H = k\frac{A\Delta t}{L}s$$

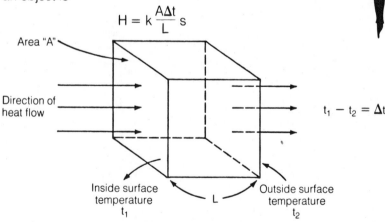

Area "A"

Direction of heat flow

$t_1 - t_2 = \Delta t$

Inside surface temperature t_1

L

Outside surface temperature t_2

In this formula A is the cross section area perpendicular to the heat transfer, L is the length, the change in temperature from one face to the other gives Δt, and s is the time interval in seconds. The thermal conductivity (k) of glass is 2.5×10^{-4} Kcal/ms C°.

Keying it in:

Press	Display	Comments
ON/c ON/c	0	Clear display and pending operations
2.5 EE 4 +/− X	2.5−04	Enter thermal conductivity
1 X 1 X	2.5−04	Enter area
( ) 5 −	5 00	Enter first temperature
0 ( )	5 00	Subtract second temperature
÷ .005 X	2.5−01	Divide by the length in meters
24 X 60 X 60	60	Multiply by 24 hours calculated in seconds
=	2.16 04	Result displayed in scientific notation
INV EE	21600	Result in Kilocalories

Complex Number Applications

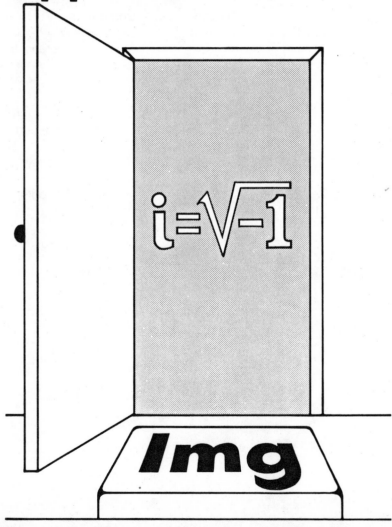

Introduction

The term "complex number" was introduced by the German mathematician Carl Friedrich Gauss (1777-1855) who paved the way for general and systematic use of complex numbers. A complex number is any number which can be written in the form x + iy where x and y are real numbers. In this standard notation for complex numbers x is called the real part, "i" is the square root of −1, and y is called the imaginary part of the number. Complex numbers can be plotted as points on a graph with the x-axis as the real axis and the y-axis as the imaginary axis. Thus the complex number z = x + iy is plotted as shown.

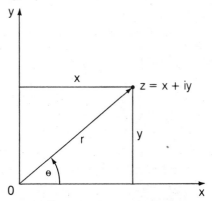

The x y plane in which the complex numbers are represented geometrically in this fashion is called the complex plane or Argand diagram (after French mathematician Jean Robert Argand, 1768-1822).

The location of a point in the complex plane can also be specified in polar form, r /θ. In this case, r is the length of the line drawn from the origin (0) to the point, and θ is the angle from the horizontal. Note that the angle θ can have an infinite number of values in rotational multiples of 360° so that 60°, 420°, 780°, and so forth, are equivalent.

COMPLEX NUMBER APPLICATIONS

4

INTRODUCTION

By applying the Pythagorean theorem to the complex number drawn in the diagram it can be shown that $r = \sqrt{x^2 + y^2}$ which is called the absolute value or modulus of the complex number. Likewise it can be shown that the argument θ of the complex number is given by $\tan \theta = y/x$. Applying trigonometry to the complex number, x is found to be equal to $r \cos \theta$, and y is found to be equal to $r \sin \theta$ thus the complex number $z = x + iy$ can be written as

$z = r \cos \theta + i\, r \sin \theta = r (\cos \theta + i \sin \theta)$.

In this chapter a few examples of applications of complex numbers are given.

Complex Roots

One of the most important complex functions is finding the roots of a complex number. If $z = w^n$ where n is an integer and $z \neq 0$, then n distinct values of w called the nth root of z can be written as

$w = \sqrt[n]{z}$

For $z = r(\cos \theta + i \sin \theta)$

$w = \sqrt[n]{z} = \sqrt[n]{r}\left[\cos (\theta + 2k\,\pi/n) + i \sin (\theta + 2k\,\pi/n)\right]$

where $k = 0, 1, ..., n - 1$

These n values lie on a circle of radius $\sqrt[n]{r}$ with the center at the origin. The points are the vertices of a regular polygon of n sides. When $k = 0$ in the above equation, the value for $\sqrt[n]{z}$ is called the principal value of the n-valued function $w = \sqrt[n]{z}$.

Your calculator has a universal root function to calculate the roots. The calculator always calculates the principal value answer. However, the other roots can also be calculated as shown below.

Target: Calculate all three roots of $\sqrt[3]{-i}$.

Tools: The principal value root is obtained using the [INV] [yˣ] key. To obtain the other two roots, add 360/n degrees (here n = 3) successively to the argument. A simple way to add 360/n degrees to the argument is to multiply the complex number (first or second root) by 1 /360/n degrees.

Keying it in: Press DRG until neither RAD or GRAD is seen in the display. This ensures that the calculator is in the degree mode.

Press	Display	Comments
ON/c ON/c	0	Clear display and pending operations
1 +/– Img	0	Enter complex number
INV y^x 3 =	0.8660254	First root with real part in display
EXC Img	−0.5	Display imaginary part
EXC Img STO 0	0.8660254	Store in memory 0. Remember the real part must be in the display before performing any operation
360 ÷ 3 =	120	360/n
θ 1 STO 1	−0.5	Remember the value is converted to rectangular form and then stored
X RCL 0 =	0	Second root with real part in display
EXC Img	1	Display imaginary part
EXC Img	0	Return real part to display before performing operation
X RCL 1 =	−0.8660254	Third root with real part in display
EXC Img	−0.5	Display imaginary part

The three roots can be graphically shown as follows.

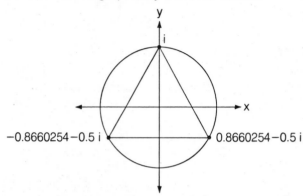

Complex Trigonometric Functions

The trigonometric values of complex numbers can be calculated using the following formulas.

$$\sin X = \frac{e^{iX} - e^{-iX}}{2i}$$

$$\cos X = \frac{e^{iX} + e^{-iX}}{2}$$

$$\tan X = \frac{\sin X}{\cos X}$$

where

$$X = a + bi$$

 Target: Find the cosine of 5 + 5i.

Tools: Using the formula for the cosine of complex numbers and the complex number mode of your calculator substitute the complex number for the x value in the formula.

Keying it in:

Press	Display	Comments
ON/c ON/c	0	Clear display and pending operations
5 Img 5	5	Enter complex number
X 1 Img =	−5	Multiply by i
INV Inx	0.0019113	Find antilogarithm, real part in display
+ 1/x	42.099201	
÷ 2 =	21.050556	Real part of result
EXC Img	71.15526	Imaginary part of result

Alternating Current Circuit Applications

Electrical circuits in which currents and voltages vary sinusoidally are called alternating current or ac circuits. Sinusoidally refers to the fact that circuits can be represented by a sine or cosine curve. When analyzing ac circuits in electrical engineering, vectors called phasors are used to represent sine waves. A phasor is a vector with magnitude A and phase angle θ in the x-y plane. The phase angle θ is positive when measured in a counterclockwise direction from the positive x-axis. A phasor rotates at a constant rate which is the angular velocity ω in radians per second. A graphical representation of a phasor and the generated sine wave is shown below. Notice that one complete revolution of the phasor generates one cycle of a sine wave.

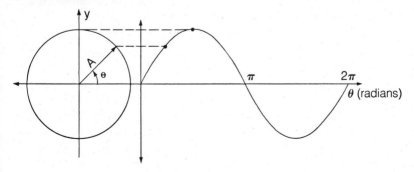

When represented as sine waves, the current and voltage in a circuit may not reach their peak values at the same time. The word "phase" is used to indicate the different positions of the current and voltage. One way to account for both the magnitude and the phase of the current or voltage is to use complex numbers. When written as a complex number, r is the value of the current or voltage and θ is a measure of the phase.

Target: Given an alternating-current with an electric current of 0.5 + 0.22j amps (when writing complex numbers in electricity, the symbol j is used rather than the symbol i), determine the magnitude of the current and the phase angle. Phasor conversions to polar form are desirable for easy multiplication and division calculations as required in IR loss or power factor computations.

Tools: The ⌊Img⌋ key is used to enter numbers in rectangular form. First enter .22 and press ⌊Img⌋ then enter .5. The CMPLX indicator is in the display. Next press ⌊INV⌋ ⌊2nd⌋ ⌊P↔R⌋ to convert the complex number to polar form. Be sure that the real portion of the number is in the display before doing the conversion sequence. *The calculator always assumes that the number in the display is the real portion when performing operations.* The value displayed after doing the conversion is the magnitude of the current. To display the phase angle, press ⌊EXC⌋ ⌊ θ ⌋.

Keying it in: Press ⌊DRG⌋ until neither RAD or GRAD is seen in the display. This ensures that the calculator is in the degree mode.

Press	Display	Comments
⌊ON/C⌋ ⌊ON/C⌋	0	Clear display and pending operations
.22 ⌊Img⌋ .5	0.5	Enter the complex number in rectangular form
⌊INV⌋ ⌊2nd⌋ ⌊P↔R⌋	0.54626	Convert to polar form. The value displayed is the magnitude of the current
⌊EXC⌋ ⌊ θ ⌋	23.749495	Display phase angle in degrees

ALTERNATING CURRENT CIRCUIT APPLICATIONS

SERIES AC CIRCUIT

A circuit may consist of several parts — resistors, inductors, and capacitors. Each of these elements offers a resistance to the flow of current in the circuit. The resistance offered by the inductor in an ac circuit is called the inductive reactance and is given by the equation $X_L = \omega L$ where ω is the angular velocity in radians per second. The resistance offered by the capacitor is called the capacitive reactance and is written as $X_C = 1/\omega C$. Since the voltage across an ideal inductor leads the inductor current by 90° and the capacitor voltage lags the capacitor current by 90°, the impedance in a series circuit is the sum of the individual impedances and can be written as

$$Z = Z_R + Z_C + Z_L$$
$$= R + j\omega L - j/\omega C$$
$$= R + j(X_L - X_C).$$

where

R = the resistor value
X_L = the inductive reactance
X_C = the capacitive reactance

When this complex number Z is converted from its rectangular form to the equivalent polar form, the r value is the impedance and the θ value indicates the phase angle between the current and the voltage.

Target: Given a circuit with a resistance of 8.0 ohms, an inductance of .02 henrys, a capacitance of .0002 farads, and a frequency of 60 hertz (cycles per second), find the impedance and the phase angle between the current and the voltage. Such circuits are called series resonance circuits because, in resonant situations, reactance of the inductance and the capacitance cancel out leaving only the resistive component. This principle is used in radio circuits to amplify voltage.

Tools: The frequency (f) given is the number of cycles completed per second. Sixty hertz is the standard frequency in the United States. The formula for calculating inductive reactance is

$$X_L = \omega L$$

where

L = the inductance in henrys

ω = the angular velocity which is 2π times the frequency in hertz.

The capacitive reactance is calculated using the formula

$$X_C = 1/\omega C$$

where

C = the capacitance in farads

ω = the angular velocity which is 2π times the frequency in hertz

After calculating the reactances, substitute these values into the formula for impedance. The result is a complex number in rectangular form. Convert this number to polar form. The magnitude of the impedance is the displayed r value. The phase angle is displayed by pressing EXC θ .

Keying it in: If RAD or GRAD is in the display, press DRG until neither is shown. This indicates that the calculator is in the degree mode. In this example, ω is calculated and stored in memory 0. The inductive reactance is stored in memory 1 to avoid rekeying it later in the solution. Be sure that the r value is in the display before storing it. The calculator always assumes that the displayed value is the real or r value.

ALTERNATING CURRENT CIRCUIT APPLICATIONS

Press	Display	Comments
[ON/c] [ON/c]	0	Clear display and pending operations
2 [×] [π] [×]	6.2831853	
60 [=] [STO] 0	376.99112	Store value of ω in memory 0
[×] .02 [=] [STO] 1	7.5398224	Calculate inductive reactance and store in memory 1
[RCL] 0 [×] .0002	0.0002	Recall ω and multiply by the capacitance
[=] [1/x]	13.262912	The reciprocal of ωC is the capacitive reactance
[+/−] [+] [RCL] 1 [=]	− 5.7230896	Subtract the capacitive reactance from the inductive reactance. The result is the imaginary portion of the impedance
[Img] 8	8	Enter the resistor value as the real portion of the complex number
[INV] [2nd] [P→R]	9.8363486	Convert to polar form. The value displayed is the impedance
[EXC] [θ]	−35.579407	Display the phase angle in degrees
[EXC] [θ] [STO] 2	8	Display impedance value again and store in memory 2 to be used in next section. (Value is converted to rectangular form when stored.)

Going further: Once the impedance has been determined, the current in the circuit can be found. Using the impedance determined above and a line voltage of 115 volts, find the current in the circuit. The formula for finding the current of a series circuit is

$$I = E \div Z$$

where
   E = the line voltage (115 volts)
   Z = the impedance

Keying it in: Remember that the calculator always converts complex numbers to their rectangular form when an operation key is pressed.

Press	Display	Comments
115 $\div$	115	Enter line voltage
RCL 2 $=$	9.508675	Divide by the recalled impedance. The result is in rectangular form
INV 2nd P↔R	11.69133	Convert to polar form. The current is in the display
EXC θ	35.579407	Display the phase angle of the current in degrees

ALTERNATING CURRENT CIRCUIT APPLICATIONS

PARALLEL CIRCUITS

A parallel circuit is a circuit which has more than one path for the current to follow. The voltage is the same across all the branches but the current divides between the branches.

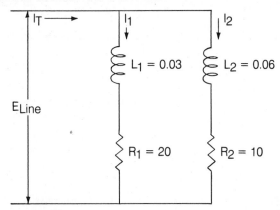

Target: Given a circuit as pictured above with resistances of 20 ohms and 10 ohms, inductances of .03 henrys and .06 henrys, a line voltage of 115 volts, and a frequency of 60 hertz, find the total current that will flow in the circuit. Solution of circuits such as these are required to determine the capacitive component needed to obtain unity power factor. Power factor correction reduces the line current and is an important consideration for power companies and their customers.

Tools: The inductive reactance is given by the inductance times ω ($2\pi f$). The impedance for each branch is then the complex number consisting of the resistance and the inductive reactance since this circuit has no capacitor. The current across a particular branch is found by dividing the line voltage by the impedance of that branch. By summing the currents across the branches, the total current is obtained.

Keying it in: Press DRG until neither RAD or GRAD is seen in the display. This ensures that the calculator is in the degree mode.

Press	Display	Comments
ON/c ON/c	0	Clear display and pending operations
2 X π X 60	60	
= STO 0	376.99112	Calculate value of ω and store it in memory 0
X .03 =	11.309734	Multiply by the first inductance to obtain the inductive reactance of the first branch
Img 20	20	Enter the resistance of the first branch in rectangular form
÷ 115 x:y	20	Enter line voltage. x:y key causes divisor and dividend to be swapped and sets up line voltage as divisor
=	4.3568026	This is the current across the first branch in rectangular form
STO 1	4.3568026	Store the first current in memory 1
.06 X RCL 0 =	22.619467	The inductive reactance of the second branch
Img 10	10	Enter the resistance of the second branch in rectangular form

(continued)

ALTERNATING CURRENT CIRCUIT APPLICATIONS

(continued)

Press	Display	Comments
÷ 115 [x:y]	10	Enter the line voltage. [x:y] key causes divisor and dividend to be swapped and sets up line voltage as divisor
[=]	1.8801901	The result is the current in the second branch in rectangular form
[+] [RCL] 1	4.3568026	Add the current in the first branch recalled from memory 1
[=]	6.2369927	The total current in rectangular form
[INV] [2nd] [P↔R]	9.1658519	Convert to polar form. The value displayed is the total current in the circuit
[EXC] [θ]	−47.120425	The phase angle of the current in degrees

Control Systems

Complex numbers find many uses in automatic control systems. Automatic control is an important and integral part of modern manufacturing and industrial processes, as well as space vehicles, missile guidance and aircraft piloting systems. The Laplace transform is a common method used in control theory. By the use of Laplace transforms, operations such as differentiation and integration can be replaced by algebraic operations in the complex plane. Thus, a linear differential equation can be transformed into an algebraic equation in a complex variable. Laplace transform allows both the transient component and steady state component of the equation to be obtained simultaneously. The following examples show how your calculator can be used to solve some control theory problems using Laplace transforms.

Example: The Laplace transformation for the output of a control system is

$$C(s) = \frac{20}{(s^2 + 4s + 13)(s + 5)}$$

Target: Find the time response (inverse transformation) of this system.

Tools: The calculator is used to obtain the partial fraction expansion of the above equation. From this partial fraction expansion, time response is then determined.

Before the partial fraction expansion can be obtained, the first term of the denominator must be factored. This can be done using the fact that the roots of the equation $ax^2 + bx + c = 0$ are given by

$$\frac{-b \pm \sqrt{b^2 - 4ac}}{2a}$$

In this example $a = 1$, $b = 4$, and $c = 13$. Therefore, using the quadratic formula, the roots are

$$\frac{-4 \pm \sqrt{4^2 - 4 \times 1 \times 13}}{2 \times 1}$$

or $-2 \pm 3j$.

So the partial fraction expansion is

$$C(s) = \frac{K_1}{s + 5} + \frac{K_2}{s + 2 - 3j} + \frac{K_{-2}}{s + 2 + 3j}$$

Now K_1, K_2, and K_{-2} must be evaluated.

Using the fact that for

$$C(s) = \frac{K}{(s - r_1)(s^2 - 2p_1s + p_1^2 + p_2^2)}$$

$$= \frac{K_1}{s - r_1} + \frac{K_2}{s - p_1 - jp_2} + \frac{K_{-2}}{s - p_1 + jp_2}$$

$K_1 = (s - r_1) \times C(s)$ as $\lim s \to r_1$

$$= \frac{K}{(s^2 - 2p_1s + p_1^2 + p_2^2)} \text{ evaluated at } s = r_1$$

and $K_2 = \dfrac{1}{2jp_2} \times (s^2 - 2p_1s + p_1^2 + p_2^2) \times C(s)$ as $\lim s \to (p_1 + jp_2)$

$$= \frac{1}{2jp_2} \times \frac{K}{(s - r_1)} \text{ evaluated at } s = (p_1 + jp_2)$$

$K_{-2} = $ conjugate of K_2

then the inverse transformation of $C(s)$ is

$$C(t) = K_1e^{r_1t} + \frac{1}{p_2} \mid K(p_1 + jp_2) \mid e^{p_1t}\sin(p_2t + \alpha)$$

where:

$K(p_1 + jp_2) = 2jp_2 \times K_2$
$\quad\quad\quad\quad\quad = K/(s - r_1)$ evaluated at $s = (p_1 + jp_2)$
$\quad\quad\quad\quad\quad$ and α is the argument of $K(p_1 + jp_2)$.

For this example, $r_1 = -5$, $p_1 = -2$, and $p_2 = 3$.

COMPLEX NUMBER APPLICATIONS

CONTROL SYSTEMS

Keying it in: If RAD or GRAD is in the display, press DRG until neither is shown. This indicates that the calculator is in the degree mode.

Press	Display	Comments
ON/c ON/c Img	0	Clear display and pending operations and enter complex number mode
2nd Fix 2	0.00	Set display to two decimal places
4 X 1 X 13 =		
+/−	−52.00	Calculate −4ac
+ 4 x² =	−36.00	
√x STO 0	0.00	Calculate $\sqrt{b^2 - 4ac}$ and store in memory 0
− 4 ÷ 2 = STO 1	−2.00	Calculate first root and store in memory 1
4 +/− − RCL 0		
÷ 2 =	−2.00	Calculate second root
5 +/− X 4 +	−20.00	
5 +/− x² + 13 =	18.00	Calculate $(s^2 - 2p_1s + p_1{}^2 + p_2{}^2)$ at $s = r_1$. Note the order in which the steps are calculated due to the chain arithmetic in the complex number mode
1/x X 20 =	1.11	Calculate K_1
RCL 1 + 5 =	3.00	Calculate $(s - r_1)$ at $s = p_1 + jp_2$
1/x X 20 =	3.33	Calculate $K(p_1 + jp_2)$
STO 2	3.33	Store $K(p_1 + jp_2)$ in memory 2
2nd Abs	4.71	Calculate $|K(p_1 + jp_2)|$
÷ 3 =	1.57	Calculate $|K(p_1 + jp_2)|/p_2$
RCL 2 2nd INV P↔R	4.71	
EXC θ	−45.00	Display α

Therefore substituting the values obtained above

$$y(t) = 1.11e^{-5t} + 1.57e^{-2t}(\sin 3t - 45°).$$

Root-Locus Plots

The basic characteristics of the transient response of a closed loop
control system are determined from the closed loop poles. The
closed loop poles are the roots of the characteristics equation of the
system. In general, finding these roots requires factoring the
characteristics polynomial, which is a laborious process for
polynomials of degree three or higher. A simple method for finding
the roots of the characteristics equation has been developed by
W. R. Evans and is used extensively in control engineering. This
method called the Root-Locus method, plots the roots of the
characteristics equation for all values of a system parameter. Your
calculator is a valuable aid in doing the tedious mathematics
involving complex numbers when working with root-locus plots.

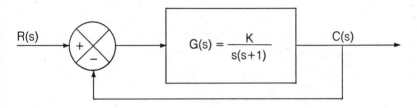

$$R(s) \quad + \bigotimes - \quad G(s) = \frac{K}{s(s+1)} \quad C(s)$$

Example: The figure shows a control system with an open loop transfer function (in Laplace transformation)

G(s) = K/s(s + 1)

Target: Determine the roots of the characteristics equations for various value of K and do a root-locus plot.

Tools: The closed loop transfer function of this system is

$$\frac{C(s)}{R(s)} = \frac{K}{s^2 + s + K}$$

The characteristics equation is $s^2 + s + K = 0$.

Your calculator will be used to determine the roots of this equation for various values of K.

The roots of quadratic equations in the form $ax^2 + bx + c = 0$ may be found using the following formula

$$\frac{-b \pm \sqrt{b^2-4ac}}{2a}$$

For this example, a = 1, b = 1, and c = K. Therefore the roots of the equation are $\dfrac{-1 \pm \sqrt{1 - 4K}}{2}$

Keying it in:

Press	Display	Comments
ON/c ON/c Img	0.00	Clear display and pending operations and enter complex number mode
INV 2nd Fix	0	Set display for floating decimal point
1 √x STO 0	1	Determine $\sqrt{b^2 - 4ac}$ for $K = 0$
+ 1 +/− ÷ 2 =	0	Determine first root for $K = 0$
EXC Img	0	Display imaginary part
1 +/− − RCL 0		
÷ 2 =	−1	Determine second root for $K = 0$
EXC Img	0	Display imaginary part
1 ÷ 8 X 4 =	0.5	
+/− + 1 =	0.5	
√x STO 0	0.7071068	Determine $\sqrt{b^2 - 4ac}$ for $K = 1/8$
+ 1 +/− ÷ 2 =	−0.1464466	Determine first root for $K = 1/8$
EXC Img	0	Display imaginary part
1 +/− − RCL 0	0.7071068	
÷ 2 =	−0.8535534	Determine second root for $K = 1/8$
EXC Img	0	Display imaginary part
1 ÷ 4 X 4 =	1	
+/− + 1 =	0	
√x STO 0	0	Determine $\sqrt{b^2 - 4ac}$ for $K = 1/4$
+ 1 +/− ÷ 2 =	−0.5	Determine first root for $K = 1/4$
EXC Img	0	Display imaginary part
1 +/− − RCL 0	0	
÷ 2 =	−0.5	Determine second root for $K = 1/4$

(continued)

(continued)

Press	Display	Comments
EXC Img	0	Display imaginary part
1 ÷ 2 X 4 =	2	
+/− + 1 =	−1	
√x STO 0	0	Determine $\sqrt{b^2 - 4ac}$ for $K = 1/2$
+ 1 +/− ÷ 2 =	−0.5	Determine first root for $K = 1/2$
EXC Img	0.5	Display imaginary part
1 +/− − RCL 0	0	
÷ 2 =	−0.5	Determine second root for $K = 1/2$
EXC Img	−0.5	Display imaginary part
1 X 4 =	4	
+/− + 1 =	−3	
√x STO 0	0	Determine $\sqrt{b^2 - 4ac}$ for $K = 1$
+ 1 +/− ÷ 2 =	−0.5	Determine first root for $K = 1$
EXC Img	0.8660254	Display imaginary part
1 +/− − RCL 0	0	
÷ 2 =	−0.5	Determine second root for $K = 1$
EXC Img	−0.8660254	Display imaginary part

The above calculated roots can be tabulated as follows.

Value	1st Root	2nd Root
0	0	−1
1/8	−0.1464466	−0.8535534
1/4	−0.5	−0.5
1/2	−0.5 + j0.5	−0.5 − j0.5
1	−0.5 + j0.8660254	−0.5 − j0.8660254

It is clear that the roots are real for K ≤ 1/4 and are complex for K > 1/4. For the various value of K, the Root-locus plot can be drawn as follows.

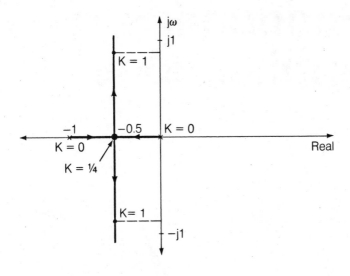

Engineering Economics Applications

SOLVING INTEREST PROBLEMS

Business and engineering professionals frequently must choose between alternate ways of doing the same project. One way of comparing the alternatives is to express the differences in monetary amounts. Engineering economics deals with this evaluation of the monetary differences in alternatives. This chapter gives a few examples of how your calculator can be applied to engineering economics problems.

Solving Interest Problems

Interest is the return obtained from the investment of capital. Compound interest formulas are frequently used in engineering economics. Your calculator is very useful in solving various types of interest problems.

Example: You plan to spend $10,000 for a plant improvement. However, this same $10,000 could alternatively be invested for the next 10 years at a 12% interest rate. Therefore, how much must this plant improvement save you per year for the next 10 years to justify the $10,000 expenditure?

 Target: Calculate the annual saving necessary to justify the $10,000 present expense.

Tools: To obtain the yearly savings necessary to justify the present expense, multiply the amount of money to be spent, $10,000, by the capital recovery factor. The capital recovery factor is calculated using the formula

$$\frac{i(1 + i)^n}{(1 + i)^n - 1}$$

where
  i = the interest rate (12%) and
  n = the number of time periods being considered (10 years).

Keying it in: If CMPLX is in the display, press INV Img. If STAT is in the display, press 2nd CSR.

Press	Display	Comments
ON/c ON/c	0	Clear display and pending operations
(1 + 12 %)	1.12	$(1 + i)$
y^x 10 = STO 0	3.1058482	$(1 + i)^n$ stored in memory 0
X 12 % ÷	0.3727018	Times i
(RCL 0 − 1 =	0.1769842	Capital recovery factor
X 10000 =	1769.8416	Annual yearly savings necessary to justify a present expense of $10,000

Since the $10,000 could earn approximately $1770 per year for the next 10 years if invested, the plant improvement needs to save at least $1770 per year to justify spending the $10,000 today.

Equivalent Uniform Annual Cash Flow

The amount which can be received from the sale of a product or service may be unaffected by the choice of alternative plans. How does one go about choosing between the alternatives in this case? One way to compare the proposed alternatives is to look at the equivalent annual cost of each plan.

Suppose you have the following facts about machines A and B.

	A	B
Purchase cost	7800	14400
Salvage value after 15 years	0	2700
Annual operating cost	1745	1200
Annual repair cost	960	540
Extra annual income taxes		320

The machines have an estimated lifetime of 15 years. You want a 10% minimum rate of return (i) after income taxes.

Target: Calculate the equivalent annual disbursements for the two machines.

Tools: Since machine A has no salvage value, the capital recovery is the purchase cost times the capital recovery factor. The capital recovery factor is calculated using the following formula

$$\frac{i(1 + i)^n}{(1 + i)^n - 1}$$

where

      i is the minimum rate of return (10%) and
      n is the number of time periods (15 years).

To find equivalent disbursements for machine A, add capital recovery, operating costs, and repair costs.

Machine B has a salvage value at the end of the 15 years so to find capital recovery for machine B, subtract the salvage value from the purchase cost, multiply that result by the capital recovery factor, and add the salvage value times 10%. To find equivalent disbursements for machine B, add the capital recovery, operating cost, repair cost, and extra annual income taxes.

Keying it in: In this example, the capital recovery factor is
calculated and stored in memory 1.

Press	Display	Comments
ON/C ON/C	0	Clear display and pending operations
(1 + 10 %)	1.1	$(1 + i)$
y^x 15 = STO 0	4.1772482	$(1 + i)^n$ stored in memory 0
X 10 % ÷	0.4177248	Times i
(RCL 0 − 1 =	0.1314738	Divide by $(1 + i)^n$ minus 1
STO 1	0.1314738	Capital recovery factor stored in memory 1
X 7800 =	1025.4955	Capital recovery for machine A
+ 1745 + 960 =	3730.4955	Total annual disbursements for machine A
14400 − 2700 =	11700	Purchase cost of machine B minus the salvage value
X RCL 1 =	1538.2432	Multiply by the capital recovery factor
+ 2700 X 10 % =	1808.2432	Capital recovery for machine B
+ 1200 + 540	540	
+ 320 =	3868.2432	Total annual disbursements for machine B

The equivalent annual disbursements for machine B are
approximately $140 more than for machine A . All other things being
equal, machine A is the most economical plan in the long run.

Depreciation

In everyday usage when depreciation is mentioned one usually thinks of the change in the value of an asset over time. From an accounting viewpoint, however, depreciation is an allocation of the cost of an asset over its lifetime. Three methods of calculating depreciation are discussed in this section. They are straight-line, sum-of-the-years-digits, and declining balance.

STRAIGHT-LINE DEPRECIATION

Straight-line depreciation is a method of uniformly distributing the cost of an asset over its lifetime. For example a machine is purchased for $35,000 and is expected to last for 20 years. After 20 years the company estimates that it will be able to sell the machine for $3,500.

 Target: Determine the straight-line depreciation amount.

Tools: The formula for calculating the straight-line depreciation amount is

$$\frac{\text{cost} - \text{estimated salvage value.}}{\text{estimated lifetime}}$$

This is the amount which is subtracted from the accounts each year as the depreciation.

Keying it in:

Press	Display	Comments
ON/c ON/c	0	Clear display and pending operations
35000 ⊟ 3500 ⊒	31500	Purchase cost minus salvage value
⊞ 20 ⊒	1575	Depreciation amount which is subtracted each year for the estimated lifetime of the machine

SUM-OF-THE-YEARS-DIGITS

Because the contributions of an asset are frequently greater during the early years of its lifetime rather than the final years, it is often desirable to depreciate a larger amount of the costs of an asset during the early years. The sum-of-the-years-digits method of calculating depreciation gives a greater depreciation in the early years of the lifetime of an asset than in the final years. By using this method, about three-fourths of the depreciable cost is written off in the first half of the estimated life of an asset.

Target: Using a purchase cost of $35,000, a salvage value of $3,500, and an estimated lifetime of 20 years, determine the sum-of-the-years-digits depreciation charge for the first three years and the final charge.

Tools: The formula for finding each years depreciation charge is

(cost − estimated salvage value) ×

$$\left(\frac{\text{estimated lifetime} + 1 - \text{year number}}{\text{sum-of-the-years-digits}} \right)$$

The sum-of-the-years-digits is found using the formula SYD = n(n + 1)÷2 where n is the estimated lifetime. In this example, the machine has an estimated lifetime of 20 years so n = 20 and the sum of the years digits is 210.

Keying it in: In this example the first cost minus the salvage value is calculated and stored in memory 0 to be recalled in calculating each depreciation charge.

Press	Display	Comments
[ON/C] [ON/C]	0	Clear display and pending operations
35000 [−] 3500 [=]	31500	Purchase cost minus salvage value
[STO] 0	31500	Store in memory 0
[×] 20 [÷] 210 [=]	3000	Depreciation for first year
[RCL] 0 [×]	31500	
19 [÷] 210 [=]	2850	Depreciation for second year
[RCL] 0 [×]	31500	
18 [÷] 210 [=]	2700	Depreciation for third year
[RCL] 0 [×]	31500	
1 [÷] 210 [=]	150	Depreciation for last year

DECLINING BALANCE

The declining balance method of depreciation also gives a greater depreciation in the early years of the lifetime of an asset. The amount which can be depreciated in the early years depends on the depreciation rate chosen.

Target: Using a first cost of $35,000, a salvage value of $3,500, an estimated lifetime of 20 years, and a depreciation rate of 200%, calculate by the declining balance method the depreciation charge for the first three years.

Tools: The formula for declining balance depreciation is

$$\text{Net book value} \times \frac{\text{depreciation rate}}{\text{estimated lifetime}}$$

The book value for the first year is the purchase cost. The book value for the second year is first cost minus the depreciation in the first year. The book value for the third year is the second year's book value minus the depreciation in the second year. Depreciation continues in this manner until the salvage value is reached at which time depreciation stops.

Keying it in:

Press	Display	Comments
ⓄN/c ⓄN/c	0	Clear display and pending operations
200 ÷ 20 = STO 0	10	
% × 35000 =	3500	Depreciation for first year
+/− + 35000 =	31500	Subtract the depreciation for the first year from the purchase cost to obtain the book value to be used in calculating the second year's depreciation
− RCL 0 %	3150	Depreciation for second year
=	28350	Depreciable value at the end of year 2
− RCL 0 %	2835	Depreciation for third year
=	25515	Depreciable value at the end of year 3

Probability in Economics

One important application of probability in engineering economy is to estimate the expected value of extreme events. Probability is the relative frequency in the long run. The expected value is the product of probability and an associated monetary amount. Suppose there is 1 chance in 20 that a certain event will occur in any given year. If the event occurs, it requires an expenditure of $30,000.

PROBABILITY IN ECONOMICS

Target: Calculate the expected value of the event happening in any year, and, assuming a minimum rate of return (i) of 8%, calculate the justifiable present expense to eliminate this risk for 10 years.

Tools: The expected value in any year is the probability (1/20) times the expense if the event occurs (30,000). The justifiable present expense to eliminate this risk for ten years is calculated by finding the present value of the expected value over the next ten years. The present value is found using the following formula

$$PV = \text{expected value} \times \frac{1 - (1 + i)^{-n}}{i}$$

where

　　n = number of periods (10 years)
　　i = minimum rate of return (8%)

Keying it in: In this example, the expected value is stored in memory 0.

Press	Display	Comments
[ON/c] [ON/c]	0	Clear display and pending operations
20 [1/x]	0.05	Enter probability
[X] 30000 [=]	1500	Multiply by expense if the event occurs to obtain expected value of event
[STO] 0	1500	Store expected value in memory 0
[(] 1 [−] [(] 1 [+]	1	
8 [%] [)]	1.08	
[y^x] 10 [+/−] [)]	0.5368065	Enter numerator
[÷] 8 [%] [=]	6.7100814	Divide by 8%
[X] [RCL] 0 [=]	10065.122	Present value

Thus $10065.12 is the justifiable present expense to eliminate this risk for the next 10 years.

Measuring & Forecasting Trends

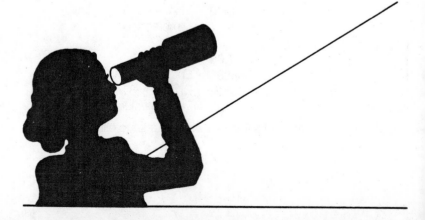

Knowledge about and some control over what will happen in the future is an important aspect of managing any type of business. The more you can predict about how prices will vary, how well a sales force will perform, how advertising will affect sales, etc., the easier it is to make sound decisions in a variety of business situations. Knowing how well one variable relates to another can allow you to make better decisions in your everyday life, as well as in your business.

The following examples illustrate some techniques that can be used to make predictions of future performance based on past records. Tools for making decisions about whether or not two variables are related and how much you can rely on the relationship are also discussed. Your calculator is equipped with special keys that make handling the mathematics involved simple. These keys perform the very useful mathematical tools that statisticians call the techniques of linear regression and correlation.

Linear Regression

The linear regression function of the calculator uses the ⟨x:y⟩ and ⟨Σ+⟩ keys, as well as the second function keys labeled ⟨Frq⟩, ⟨Corr⟩, ⟨b/a⟩, ⟨x'⟩, and ⟨y'⟩.

In linear regression the calculator mathematically draws the best fitting line through a series of data points. To enable it to do this, key in the data with the ⟨x:y⟩, ⟨Σ+⟩, and ⟨2nd⟩ ⟨Frq⟩ keys. The basic elements of how these keys are used were discussed in Chapter 1. In this chapter the processes are reviewed in more detail. The techniques described in this chapter allow you to make predictions on any process or operation that can be assumed to follow a straight line pattern of behavior.

Example: Suppose you have data about some type of process or operation, and need to make predictions based on this data. Data such as this is often expressed in terms of pairs of numbers labeled with the letters "x" and "y", such as those tabulated below. The points could be plotted as shown:

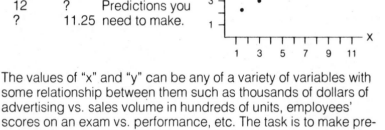

x	y	
1.5	2.25	
3.0	3.0	Five data
4.25	5.5	points you
6.0	3.5	know
8.0	7.0	
12	?	Predictions you
?	11.25	need to make.

The values of "x" and "y" can be any of a variety of variables with some relationship between them such as thousands of dollars of advertising vs. sales volume in hundreds of units, employees' scores on an exam vs. performance, etc. The task is to make predictions based on the data. Typical things you might need to know in this case could be:

For a given "x" value (say x = 12), what is the value of "y"? or For what "x" value will "y" reach some specific number (say 11.25)?

You might also like to know how accurate the predictions are, as well as how to make additional predictions at a later time.

NOTE: Caution should be used in computing an "x" (independent) value on the basis of a "y" (dependent) value. Further, it is not valid to compute a "y" value on the basis of an "x" which is outside the range of the entered "x" values. The predictions which result do not have statistical validity, and the probability figures that are found are not valid. However, trend line analysis and forecasting calculations often use these computations to make predictions or estimations of probability about the future. When performing such calculations, the actual values may differ from the calculated values.

Keying it in: If CMPLX is displayed, press INV Img. If STAT is displayed, press 2nd CSR. Then enter the information (the data) as follows: enter each "x" value, press x:y, enter the corresponding "y" value, then press Σ+. Repeat the process for all the data.

For the data tabulated in the example:

Press	Display	Comments
ON/C ON/C 2nd CSR	0	Clear display, pending operations, and statistical registers
1.5 x:y 2.25 Σ+	1	Also displayed is STAT after pressing Σ+
3 x:y 3 Σ+	2	Notice that the calculator
4.25 x:y 5.5 Σ+	3	keeps track of how many
6 x:y 3.5 Σ+	4	data points (pairs of "x"
8 x:y 7 Σ+	5	and "y" values) are entered

To predict a "y" value for a given "x" value, enter the "x" value, and press 2nd y'.

Press	Display	Comments
12 2nd y'	8.8882025	The "y" value when "x" = 12

There is a slight pause when you press the y' key before the result is displayed. That is because the calculator is working through the linear regression calculation. Here is the formula.

$$y' = \left[\frac{\dfrac{\Sigma x_i \, \Sigma y_i}{N} - \Sigma x_i y_i}{\dfrac{(\Sigma x_i)^2}{N} - \Sigma x_i^2} \right] \times (\text{your "x" value})$$
$$+ \left\{ \frac{\Sigma y_i}{N} - \left[\frac{\dfrac{\Sigma x_i \, \Sigma y_i}{N} - \Sigma x_i y_i}{\dfrac{(\Sigma x_i)^2}{N} - \Sigma x_i^2} \right] \left(\frac{\Sigma x_i}{N} \right) \right\}$$

To find an "x" value for a given "y" value, enter the "y" value, then press 2nd x'.

Press	Display	Comments
11.25 2nd x'	15.79358	The "x" value for "y" = 11.25

The Correlation Coefficient

The [2nd] [Corr] key sequence displays the linear correlation coefficient of the two sets of data ("x"s and "y"s). A value close to positive 1 indicates a high positive relationship and a value close to minus 1 indicates a high negative relationship. As the value gets closer to zero the two sets of data become less related. Note that it is possible that "x" and "y" might have a nonlinear relationship even if the linear correlation coefficient is near zero. This chapter, however, discusses only linear relationships.

To find out how well the data correlates press [2nd] [Corr]. The correlation coefficient for the line is then displayed. For the example:

Press	Display	Comments
[2nd] [Corr]	0.8097825	Correlation coefficient

Caution: Cause and Effect

Be careful about drawing conclusions about cause and effect. Two variables that are related to a third can show a relationship to each other without a "cause and effect" relationship between them.

For example, you may have data on children that relates manual dexterity (the time to finish a jigsaw puzzle) to mathematical ability (performance on a math test). There may be a high correlation coefficient. Further analysis may show, however, that the older children display both better manual coordination and mathematical skill and that if the sample is restructured to include only children of the same age an entirely different relationship may result. So be careful about applying results in making decisions. Consider the makeup of the sample and exactly what is being measured and tested.

CHAPTER 6

Slope and Intercept

To find out more about the line, press [2nd] [b/a] and [x:y] to display
the intercept and slope of the line.

Press	Display	Comments
[2nd] [b/a]	1.4172723	Intercept
[x:y]	0.6225775	Slope

The slope of the line is the ratio of its "rise" to its "run," while the intercept is the point where the line crosses the y axis. Any straight
line may be expressed as an equation written in the form:

$y = ax + b$
where a is the slope value and b is the intercept value.

Using the calculated values, write an equation for the line best fitting the data as follows:

$y = (.62)x + 1.42$ (The slope and intercept have been
rounded.)

This equation can now be used to predict a "y" value for any selected "x" value with a simple calculation at some future time, without
reentering all the data.

Summary

The following diagram illustrates all of the information discussed so far.

After entering the x,y coordinates of the known values

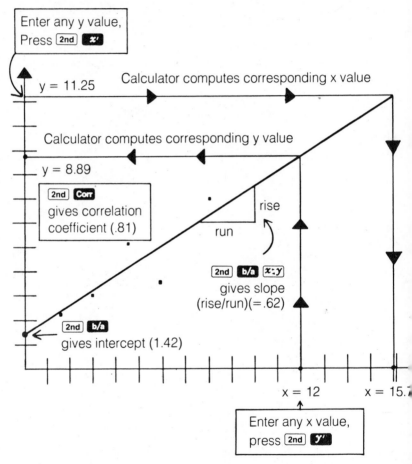

Enter any y value,
Press [2nd] [x']

y = 11.25   Calculator computes corresponding x value

Calculator computes corresponding y value

y = 8.89

[2nd] [Corr]
gives correlation
coefficient (.81)

rise

run

[2nd] [b/a] [x:y]
gives slope
(rise/run)(=.62)

[2nd] [b/a]
gives intercept (1.42)

x = 12   x = 15.7

Enter any x value,
press [2nd] [y']

The rest of the chapter gives a few examples of how these procedures can be used.

Predicting Sales from Advertising (Linear Regression)

Suppose a company recently started advertising in a new medium (say a series of magazines), on a weekly basis. The marketing manager has a record of the amount spent on advertising each week ("x") and the corresponding sales volume ("y"). The question is: What is the expected sales volume if $3250 is spent on magazine advertising next week?

Amount Spent on Advertising ("x")	Weekly Sales Volume ("y")
$1000	101,000
$1250	126,000
$1500	163,000
$2000	194,000
$2500	209,000
$3250	?

Target: Predict what will happen, in unit sales ("y"), if the advertising budget ("x") is increased to $3250, using the best straight line approximation.

Tools: You will be using the linear regression feature of the calculator to help predict the result. First, enter the information:

Enter $ in advertising:
   press ⌷x:y⌷
Enter corresponding unit sales:
   press ⌷Σ+⌷

To make the prediction, enter the trial advertising dollar value and press ⌷2nd⌷ ⌷y'⌷ .

NOTE: As you get further outside the range of the known "x" values, the reliability of the corresponding "y" value decreases.

To find out how well the data correlates to the straight line drawn through the data points, press ⌷2nd⌷ ⌷Corr⌋ to display the correlation coefficient. A value near 1 means a fairly good linear correlation.

Keying it in: First, enter the data:

Press	Display	Comments
ON/c ON/c 2nd CSR	0	Clear display, pending operations, and statistics registers

Enter the 5 data points:

	Display	
1000 x:y 101000 Σ+	1	
1250 x:y 126000 Σ+	2	The calculator displays the
1500 x:y 163000 Σ+	3	number of (x,y) points that
2000. x:y 194000 Σ+	4	have been entered
2500 x:y 209000 Σ+	5	

Now find the "y" value for "x" = $3250

3250 2nd **y'**	274517.24	

Based on the best straight line approximation, the projected weekly sales volume for $3250 spent on advertising is approximately 274,500 units. This is assuming there is no change in the relationship of "x" to "y" over time.

Now to see how good an estimate the calculator has made:

Press	Display	Comments
2nd Corr	0.9637964	

The correlation is good, but the small number of points used and the distance that 3250 is outside the other "x" values make this less significant.

Decision time: You are now in a position to make predictions about future sales based on advertising. The correlation coefficient seems to indicate that the prediction will be a good one, but re-

member the total number of data points is small. There are only 5 points upon which to predict the future. There is a way to further analyze the correlation that allows you to take the number of data points into account (see the Correlation Coefficient Significance Section).

To make a decision at this point, take a look at the increased cost and weigh that against the increase in sales that you predict will result.

Press	Display	Comments
ON/C ON/C	0	Clear display and pending operations
3250 − 2500 =	750	Amount of advertising increase
274517.24 − 209000 =	65517.24	Increase in unit sales predicted.

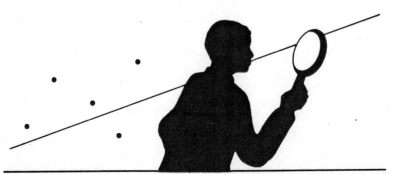

Correlation Coefficient Significance

As previously mentioned, in this example you are predicting the future based on only five data points from the past. That is not much to go on. In general, the less data you have to go on, the less reliable the prediction. You want to know if there is a significant possibility that such a large value as this correlation coefficient could be due to chance alone. There is a quick way to get a measure of how significant the correlation coefficient is under different data conditions. (As a general rule, if there is not much data, unless the correlation coefficient is quite close to plus or minus one, you cannot be too sure of it).

One procedure for a quick check on the significance of the correlation coefficient is as follows:

a) Decide on how sure you would like (or need) the correlation coefficient to be, say 95%.

b) Locate the r_{test} (test correlation coefficient) value from the table at the end of this chapter for the degree of certainty selected and the number of samples used.

c) If the calculated correlation coefficient is greater than the r_{test} value, you can be certain (to the degree selected) that the calculated correlation coefficient was not due to chance alone.

For the previous example, the calculated correlation coefficient is 0.96. Compare this to the r_{test} value; at 95% certainty for 5 samples (find this value in the tables):

$$r_{test} = .878$$

Since the correlation coefficient is greater than r_{test}, it is correct to assume that the correlation coefficient is not due to chance alone with a 95% degree of certainty. (Being 95% certain of a conclusion means that 95 times out of 100 you will be correct).

NOTE: Since the "x" value used for prediction (3250) is outside the range of "x" values entered, this degree of certainty is not statistically accurate. It is, however, an indication of the certainty.

Earnings Per Share Projections (Trend Line Analysis)

In many instances data is collected in the form of a series of yearly figures, and you need to predict what will happen in subsequent years. This type of prediction involves what statisticians call trend line analysis. Trend line analysis is a special type of linear regression. The calculator has features that make trend line analysis easy.

Example: A stock has reported the following earnings per share during the past few years:

> $1.52 in 1976
> $1.35 in 1977
> $1.53 in 1978
> $2.17 in 1979
> $3.60 in 1980

You would like to predict the earnings per share for the next three years. You would also like to know in what year you could expect the earnings per share to reach $6.50.

Target: You wish to enter the data you have into the calculator, and then use trend line analysis to make predictions. You would also like to know how well the two sets of data correlate.

Tools: First, enter the data, using the $\boxed{x\colon y}$ and $\boxed{\Sigma+}$ keys. In this case the "x" values are a series of years in sequence, and the "y" values are the earnings per share recorded for each year. (Data for a series of successive years is common in trend line analysis situations.)

In trend line analysis, the calculator automatically adds 1 to the "x" variable.

> Enter the first "x" value (the first year, 1976) and press $\boxed{x\colon y}$, then enter a "y" value ($1.52 earnings per share) and press $\boxed{\Sigma+}$. The first data point is entered.

Then:

> Enter the second data point by just entering the "y" value (for this example $1.35) and pressing $\boxed{\Sigma+}$. The calculator automatically increments the "x" variable by 1.

After the data is entered:

To make predictions on earnings for future years:
Enter the year and press [2nd] **y'**

To predict in what year a certain level of earnings per share will be reached:
Enter the earnings and press [2nd] **x'**

To see how well the two sets of data correlate:
Press [2nd] **Corr**

Keying it in:

Press	Display	Comments
[ON/c] [ON/c] [2nd] **CSR**	0	Clear display, pending operations, and statistical registers
[2nd] **Fix** 2	0.00	This sets the display to show only two decimal places.

Now enter the data:

	Display	
1976 [x:y] 1.52 [Σ+]	1.00	Note: the calculator
1.35 [Σ+]	2.00	increases the "x" value by 1
1.53 [Σ+]	3.00	automatically unless another
2.17 [Σ+]	4.00	value is entered
3.6 [Σ+]	5.00	

Decision Time: To predict the earnings for future years (future "y" values) key in the year, and press [2nd] **y'** :

Press	Display	Comments
1981 [2nd] **y'**	3.53	Earnings of $3.53 per share are projected for 1981
1982 [2nd] **y'**	4.03	For 1982
1983 [2nd] **y'**	4.52	For 1983

You can now make decisions based on the pattern of growth you are watching or predict when the earnings per share will reach a specified value. For example, to calculate when the earnings will reach $6.50 (if the earning trend continues), enter 6.5 and press
[2nd] [x']

Press	Display	Comments
6.5 [2nd] [x']	1986.97	About 1987

Going further: To see how well the two sets of data are correlated just press [2nd] [Corr].

Press	Display	Comments
[2nd] [Corr]	0.85	

Note that in this example the use of the r_{test} values to determine the significance of the correlation coefficient is not really valid. When determining results like the r_{test} values, one of the assumptions made is that both variables are distributed randomly with normal distribution. Since "x" in this example can only be sequential year values it is not a random variable.

A statistic that can be used with this example, however, is the coefficient of determination. The coefficient of determination is the square of the correlation coefficient. It expresses the proportion of variation in "y" explained by "x". In this example, r = .85 and r^2 = .72. Therefore 72% of the variance in "y" has been explained by the knowledge of "x".

Relating Job Performance to Test Score (Establishing Correlation)

In this example the linear regression feature of the calculator, particularly the correlation feature (2nd Corr), is used to help make a decision on whether two variables are related. It may appear that one factor is related to another, but how closely they relate may be unclear. With the calculator, you can get a more accurate picture of the relationship between two variables.

Example: Suppose your sales manager is spending a considerable sum on a test for prospective sales employees. See if this test is actually telling you anything about how well the employee will function in the field. Does a higher test score mean superior sales performance? How strong a correlation is there between these two factors in your business?

You have samples of the test scores for 10 employees, along with records on sales performance expressed as the percentage of the time that each employee exceeded his or her weekly sales goals last year. The data is tabulated below:

Employee	Employee Test Score ("x")	Employee Sales Performance ("y")
Lane	5	10
Bob	13	30
Britt	8	30
Ralph	10	40
Lana	15	60
Dae	20	50
Dennis	4	20
Patrick	16	60
Kathy	18	50
Kevin	6	20

Target: Determine if there is a relationship between test scores and sales performance. If so, what is the relationship, and how reliable is it?

Tools: The calculator's linear regression feature can easily apply some complicated statistical mathematics to this problem. First enter the data with the x:y and Σ+ keys. Then study the correlation coefficient (r) by pressing 2nd Corr, and consulting the "r_test" table at the end of this chapter.

Keying it in: Enter the data and determine the correlation co-efficient.

Press	Display	Comments
[ON/c] [ON/c] [2nd] **CSR**	0.00	Clear display, pending opera-tions, and statistical registers
5 [x:y] 10 [Σ+]	1.00	
13 [x:y] 30 [Σ+]	2.00	
8 [x:y] 30 [Σ+]	3.00	
10 [x:y] 40 [Σ+]	4.00	
15 [x:y] 60 [Σ+]	5.00	
20 [x:y] 50 [Σ+]	6.00	
4 [x:y] 20 [Σ+]	7.00	
16 [x:y] 60 [Σ+]	8.00	
18 [x:y] 50 [Σ+]	9.00	
6 [x:y] 20 [Σ+]	10.00	

To find the correlation coefficient:

[2nd] **Corr** 0.87 = r

 Decision Time: The correlation coefficient of 0.87 indicates that there is a relatively high relationship between the test scores and the indicator for employee performance.

To determine how significant this correlation coefficient is, look at the table at the end of this chapter. Find the line for the number of samples (in this case 10) and examine the "r_{test}" values listed to the right. The value for r (the correlation coefficient: 0.87) falls between .765 and .872 listed on the table, so you can be between 99% and 99.9% confident that the correlation coefficient was not due to chance alone.

Going further: Using the data in the calculator, employee performance can be predicted for any given test score. To do this, key in the score ("x") value and press [2nd] **y'** . Some examples:

Press	Display	Comments
7 [2nd] **y'**	24.92	
25 [2nd] **y'**	73.23	
30 [2nd] **y'**	86.65	

If you wish to make predictions again at a later date, write down the equation of the line the calculator has drawn through the data using the [2nd] **b/a** and **x:y** key sequences:

Press	Display	Comments
[2nd] **b/a**	6.14	Intercept value (b)
x:y	2.68	Slope value (a)

The equation of any straight line can be expressed as:

$y = ax + b$
$y = (Slope) \times (x) + (Intcp)$; so in this case the line is given by
$y = 2.68 \times (x) + 6.14$

If you wish to make a prediction, you need to note the slope and intercept values. If an employee then scores 24 on the test, you can substitute that result for "x" in the equation to predict his or her performance.

Press	Display	Comments
[ON/c] [ON/c]	0	Clear display and pending operations
2.68 [X] 24 [+] 6.14 [=]	70.46	

MEASURING & FORECASTING TRENDS   CHAPTER
HOW TO USE "r_{test}" TABLE FOR
CORRELATION COEFFICIENTS   **6**

How to Use "r_{test}" Table for Correlation Coefficients

Find the number of samples in the left hand column, and scan across to the right, comparing the values of r_{test} listed in the table to the calculated correlation coefficient. Find the values of r_{test} that the correlation coefficient lies between and scan upward to read the "degree of certainty" limits for the coefficient. If the correlation coefficient is too small to find in the table, then you are less than 80% sure of its significance. For negative correlation coefficients, take the absolute value of the correlation coefficient and find that value in the table.

The values in this table are from the formula:

$$r_{test} = \left(\frac{t^2}{t^2 + df} \right)^{1/2}$$

where df = the degrees of freedom, and t is the t value for df from table C in the Appendix.

Example: For 15 samples, a correlation coefficient of .525 can be considered between 95% and 99% significant.

Table of "r_{test}" Values — Test Values for Correlation Coefficient

# of Samples	(df) degrees of Freedom	80%	90%	95%	99%	99.9%
3	1	.951	.988	.997	1.000	1.000
4	2	.800	.900	.950	.990	.999
5	3	.687	.805	.878	.959	.991
6	4	.608	.729	.811	.917	.974
7	5	.551	.669	.755	.875	.951
8	6	.507	.621	.707	.834	.925
9	7	.472	.582	.666	.798	.898
10	8	.443	.549	.632	.765	.872
11	9	.419	.521	.602	.735	.847
12	10	.398	.497	.576	.708	.823
13	11	.380	.476	.553	.684	.801
14	12	.365	.457	.532	.661	.780
15	13	.351	.441	.514	.641	.760
16	14	.338	.426	.497	.623	.742
17	15	.327	.412	.482	.606	.725
18	16	.317	.400	.468	.590	.708
19	17	.308	.389	.456	.575	.693
20	18	.299	.378	.444	.561	.679
21	19	.291	.369	.433	.549	.665
22	20	.284	.360	.423	.537	.652
23	21	.277	.352	.413	.526	.640
24	22	.271	.344	.404	.515	.629
25	23	.265	.337	.396	.505	.618
26	24	.260	.330	.388	.496	.607
27	25	.255	.323	.381	.487	.597
28	26	.250	.317	.374	.479	.588
29	27	.245	.311	.367	.471	.579
30	28	.241	.306	.361	.463	.570
31	29	.237	.301	.355	.456	.562
32	30	.233	.296	.349	.449	.554
42	40	.202	.257	.304	.393	.490
62	60	.165	.211	.250	.325	.408
122	120	.117	.150	.178	.232	.294

Testing
Claims

Introduction

Many times in business, science, or everyday life you must make decisions about accepting or buying large quantities of items. Time and expense usually only allow examination and testing of a few samples. This is often the case in an "incoming quality control" operation, for example.

Whenever deciding about a large population based on a small sample, a certain amount of uncertainty is present. When a manufacturer claims that goods meet a certain specification, data from the sample can be used to test that claim to a specified degree of certainty.

The examples in this chapter explore the examination and analysis of data from samples and relating that data to larger populations. Complex statistical methods are involved, but with the calculator doing the mathematics, the implementation of these techniques is quite simple.

In most of the examples in this chapter the following situation is addressed:

A manufacturer (grower/supplier, etc.) makes a claim about a particular specification for a shipment of goods he has just delivered. This claim usually is expressed as a mean value for the population:
> "The mean weight of product in these containers is 510 grams."
> "The mean lifetime of these batteries under standard load conditions is 180 hours."

To check the claim made, test as large a sample as possible, given the time and expense limitations. Then use the test data to determine and analyze the mean value and standard deviation. Your calculator has keys that make this calculation quite easy. Take the measured sample data and enter it with the ⎡Σ+⎤ key. The ⎡2nd⎤ ⎡Mean⎤ and ⎡2nd⎤ ⎡σn-1⎤ keys give the mean and standard deviation of the sample data and the first step in the decision. Is the mean close to the claimed value? Is the standard deviation large or small? If the mean is significantly lower than the claimed value, or there is a large standard deviation, indicating a highly varying value for the parameter you are examining, that may be enough reason to reject the shipment immediately.

The rest of this chapter shows the use of statistical inferences in calculator decision making based on sample results. These are important concepts: The *population* refers to the entire set of items under consideration; the *sample* is a part of the population that has been chosen to be tested. You will be making decisions about the population based on sample data and the *level of certainty* chosen.

Mean Weight of Aerosol Dispensers

This example involves testing the manufacturer's claim with concern about both the upper and lower limits.

A large shipment (population) of aerosol cans of insecticide has arrived at your receiving dock. The manufacturer claims that the cans contain, on the average, 510 grams of insecticide. You would like to be sure that he is meeting this claim.

You are concerned about this problem for two reasons: These particular cans do not work properly if they are too full; and you are not getting what you paid for if they are less than full. Ideally, each can contains exactly 510 grams.

Have a technician measure the weight of 40 cans (the sample) and tabulate the data. With a quick calculation on the calculator you find:

The mean sample weight is 508.75g (usually labeled $\bar{x}$)
The sample standard deviation (labeled s_x) is 19.97g

The decision: Is the manufacturer meeting his claim? Should you accept the shipment or reject it? Can the sample data give you more information on which to base your decision?

Target: Suppose you want to be 95% sure that the manufacturer has *not* met his claim before you reject the shipment. The target here is to get as much information as possible about the population, based on the data from the sample.

 Tools: The sample size is over 30 items, which statisticians generally agree is an informal boundary between "large" and "small" samples. For the "large" sample of 40 items you may assume that the sample standard deviation (s_x) is an acceptable estimate of the population standard deviation (usually labeled with the lower case Greek letter sigma, σ).

This information often allows reaching some important conclusions immediately. Most manufacturing processes deviate from the specified or target value in a "normal" way, so the population values can be considered to follow the "normal curve." This means that about 95% of the cans will be within ±2 standard deviations of the mean. The sample standard deviation of 19.97 implies a range of almost 80 grams (from 39.94 below the mean to 39.94 above the mean) for about 95% of the cans. If a ±40 gram variation from the mean in the weight of the cans is by itself unacceptable, you might reject the cans based on the standard deviation value alone.

If the standard deviation value is acceptable, continue with the analysis.

a) Select a degree of certainty for the decision to accept or reject, in this instance 95%.

b) Establish a range within the population mean (labeled with the Greek letter mu, μ), to a particular degree of certainty. The formula for this range is:

$$\text{Range for } \mu \text{ at degree of certainty selected} = \bar{x} \pm \frac{\sigma}{\sqrt{n}} z$$

In this formula $\bar{x}$ is the sample mean, n is the number of samples, and z is the "z score" for the selected degree of certainty. This "z score" can be found in Table A in the Appendix, in column II where z values for checking both upper and lower levels are tabulated. In this table, column II reads a z value of 1.96 at a 95% degree of certainty.

Summarizing:

From Table A: z = 1.96

$\sigma = s_x = 19.97$ (for large samples only, n > 30)

n = 40

$\bar{x} = 508.75$,

and you need to evaluate $\bar{x} \pm \frac{\sigma}{\sqrt{n}} z$.

Keying it in: A good way to begin this calculation is to evaluate the last term $\dfrac{\sigma}{\sqrt{n}}z$ and store it in memory 0.

Press	Display	Comments
[ON/c] [ON/c] [2nd] **Fix** 2	0.00	Clear display and pending operations and set display to two decimal places
[2nd] **CSR**	0.00	Clear statistics registers
19.97 [÷] 40 [√x] [X]	3.16	This evaluates $\dfrac{\sigma}{\sqrt{n}}z$
1.96 [=] [STO] 0	6.19	and stores it
[+] 508.75 [=]	514.94	Next, evaluate $\bar{x} + \dfrac{\sigma}{\sqrt{n}}z$
508.75 [−] [RCL] 0 [=]	502.56	Evaluate $\bar{x} - \dfrac{\sigma}{\sqrt{n}}z$

The manufacturer's claimed value of 510g falls inside these limits; therefore the claim can be accepted.

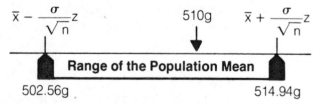

The sample indicates that the population mean is between these two numbers, with 95% certainty.

MEAN WEIGHT OF AEROSOL DISPENSERS

Decision time: You now have more information about the shipment based on the sample results. The mean weight value for the shipment (the whole population) lies between 502.56 grams

and 514.94 grams, with 95% certainty. Since the manufacturer's claimed weight value of 510 grams falls within these limits, as far as you can tell from the sample he has met his claim. Based on this analysis, accept the shipment of aerosol cans.

The analysis is summarized here:

a) Get as large a sample as possible and measure it; calculate the sample mean ($\overline{x}$) and standard deviation (s_x).

b) Choose the degree of certainty needed and calculate the predicted range for the population mean with the formula below:

$$\text{Range for } \mu = \overline{x} \pm \frac{\sigma}{\sqrt{n}}z$$

Find z from column II in Table A for the selected degree of certainty. For samples with over 30 items, approximate σ with s_x.

c) If the manufacturer's claim value falls inside the range, accept, and vice versa.

Further notes: When selecting the degree of certainty for a problem, it is important to know how the statistical process works. The amount of information in the sample does not change. If a very high degree of certainty is selected, then what you are certain about is less definite. Here is an example: A mechanic looks at your car and says it will cost about $80 to $100 to fix it. If you tell him to be 99% sure of his estimate, he will probably estimate a wider range, perhaps $50 to $200. If the situation under investigation demands more certainty about a smaller range, then a larger sample must be taken.

Mean Battery Lifetime

This example involves testing a manufacturer's claim with concern about meeting the minimum specifications only.

The manufacturer of an electronic product requires a battery. A supplier has shipped 5000 batteries, and claims the mean lifetime for this shipment (population) is 180 hours. The manufacturer wants to check on the supplier's claim. Critical to the decision to accept the shipment is that the mean lifetime of the shipment of batteries is no less than 180 hours.

To test the population of 5000 (N) batteries, have a technician select a sample (n) of 100 batteries and measure the average lifetime under standard load conditions. Since this test ruins the batteries, expense determines the sample size. The technician finds that the sample mean lifetime ($\bar{x}$) is 175 hours, with a sample standard deviation (s_x) of 18 hours. The decision: Accept or reject the shipment?

Since the sample of 100 batteries qualifies as a "large" one ($n > 30$), the sample standard deviation (s_x) is considered to be equal to the population standard deviation (σ). So an immediate decision becomes: Is the standard deviation of the shipment acceptable? In this case, $\sigma = 18$ hours. Suppose this variability is acceptable. Then a judgment must be made about the population mean (μ). The sample mean ($\bar{x}$) is 175 hours. How can this information be used to draw a conclusion about the population mean lifetime?

Target: Suppose the manufacturer wants to be 95% certain not to reject good batteries. The primary concern is that the battery life be not much less than 180 hours.

Tools: A formula from statistics allows calculating, from sample data, a range in which the population mean will lie. With this range, based on the sample data and degree of certainty, an upper and a lower limit for the actual population mean can be found.

The formula is:

$$\text{Range for population mean} = \bar{x} \pm \left[\frac{(N - n)}{(N - 1)}\right]^{1/2} \frac{\sigma}{\sqrt{n}} z$$

(This formula is complex, but it is easy to evaluate on the calculator.)

In this case: $\bar{x}$ is the sample mean lifetime = 175 hours;
N is the population size = 5000;
n is the sample size = 100;
σ is the standard deviation of the population, which in this case
   can be approximated by s_x (= 18 hours);
   and,
z is the z value found in Appendix Table A, for the degree of certainty selected (95%), taken from column I, since rejection is based on only the lower boundary in this case. The value of z is 1.65.

A note here: In this formula the expression $\left[\frac{(N - n)}{(N - 1)}\right]^{1/2}$

is a factor which allows for the fact that when batteries in the sample are tested, they are removed from the population and cannot be returned after the test. This removal of sample items affects the "randomness" of the selection, and this factor corrects for this fact.

Keying it in: In doing this calculation, first evaluate the quantity

$$\left[\frac{(N - n)}{(N - 1)}\right]^{½} \frac{\sigma}{\sqrt{n}} z \text{ and store it.}$$

Press	Display	Comments
ON/c ON/c	0	Clear display and pending operations
2nd Fix 2	0.00	Fix decimal to two places
((5000 − 100)	4900.00	
÷ (5000 − 1)	4999.00	
) √x̄ × 18 ÷ 100	100	
√x̄ × 1.65 = STO 0	2.94	The deviation
+ 175 =	177.94	Upper limit
175 − RCL 0 =	172.06	Lower limit

Decision time: The population mean is therefore predicted to have a value somewhere between 172.06 and 177.94. Thus, with 95% certainty, it can be said that the population mean is not

greater than 177.94. So, based on the sample data, the battery mean lifetime is less than 180 hours, and based on this analysis the shipment should be rejected, or the vendor should be talked to about correcting the problem.

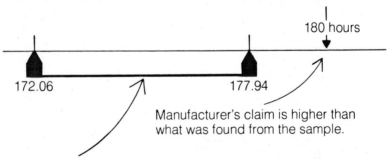

180 hours

172.06   177.94

Manufacturer's claim is higher than what was found from the sample.

The actual value of the population mean is predicted to be in this range, lower than the 180 hour lifetime needed (and claimed by the manufacturer).

The Tint in Paint Mix

This example involves testing a claim using data from a small sample with concern about both upper and lower limits.

A check is being made on a formulating process in a paint manufacturing operation concerning the amount of red dye being mixed into 5 gallon containers of rose colored paint. The process specification calls for 15.5 ounces of red tint in each can. To perform the check, select a random sample of 8 cans. Through analysis the tint content is found to be:

15.2 oz	15.8 oz
15.0 oz	16.1 oz
15.7 oz	15.6 oz
15.9 oz	15.9 oz

The analysis is expensive, so a small sample quantity is all that can be analyzed. The decision in this case: Should manufacturing be stopped and the process be adjusted?

Target: Get as much information as possible about the population mean for the amount of red tint, based on data from the small sample. To do this, use a statistica! technique especially designed to handle the "small sample" situation. This technique calculates a predicted range of values within which the population mean (μ) will fall, with a selected degree of certainty.

This predicted range of values can form the basis for a decision. If the calculated range of values includes the specification value of 15.5 oz., there is not enough indication of trouble to stop production. If the range of values calculated from the sample data does not include the specification value, however, it is sure (to the degree of certainty selected) that there is a problem and an adjustment should be made. The concern is about both limits on the amount of tint; too much will give a color that is too red, while too little tint will provide too weak a color.

TESTING CLAIMS

THE TINT IN PAINT MIX

Tools: Since the sample size in this case is less than 30, it is classified as a small sample and statistical methods especially suited to this situation should be used. First, decide on a degree of certainty needed for the decision, for instance 90%. Then, calculate the predicted range for the mean tint (population value) using the formula below.

Predicted Range for
Population Mean $\mu = \bar{x} \pm \dfrac{s_x}{\sqrt{n}}t$

where $\bar{x}$ is the mean value for the sample;

s_x is the sample standard deviation;

n is the size of the sample;

and,

t is a value found from Table C in the Appendix for the degree of certainty selected (90%), and the number of degrees of freedom (df) for the problem. In this case df = (n − 1) = 7. Table C gives a t value of 1.895

To find the sample mean ($\bar{x}$) and sample standard deviation (s_x), use special keys on the calculator.

Keying it in: First, clear the calculator and enter the sample data with the $\boxed{\Sigma +}$ key:

Press	Display	Comments
$\boxed{ON/C}$ $\boxed{ON/C}$ $\boxed{2nd}$ $\boxed{CSR}$	0	Clear display and pending operations. If necessary, clear the statistical registers
$\boxed{2nd}$ $\boxed{Fix}$ 2	0.00	Fix decimal to two places
15.2 $\boxed{\Sigma +}$	1.00	The display keeps track
15 $\boxed{\Sigma +}$	2.00	of the number of data
15.7 $\boxed{\Sigma +}$	3.00	entries
15.9 $\boxed{\Sigma +}$	4.00	
15.8 $\boxed{\Sigma +}$	5.00	
16.1 $\boxed{\Sigma +}$	6.00	
15.6 $\boxed{\Sigma +}$	7.00	
15.9 $\boxed{\Sigma +}$	8.00	

Now calculate the sample mean and standard deviation.

Press	Display	Comments
2nd Mean	15.65	The sample mean, $\bar{x}$
2nd σn-1	0.37	The sample standard deviation, s_x

The sample mean is near 15.5, and the standard deviation is low, indicating that there is a relatively low variation to the measured sample red tint values. But the sample is a small one, and an important decision must be made about a much larger population based on it. This is where the statistical method can be helpful. Now calculate the predicted range of the population mean (μ).

$$\text{Predicted Range} = \bar{x} \pm \frac{s_x}{\sqrt{n}} \, t$$

Now you know that $\bar{x} = 15.65 \quad n = 8$
$s_x = 0.37 \quad t = 1.895$

Begin by calculating $\dfrac{s_x}{\sqrt{n}} \, t$

Press	Display	Comments
ON/c ON/c	0.00	Clear display and pending operations
.37 ÷ 8 $\sqrt{x}$ X	0.13	
1.895 = STO 0	0.25	Now add this to $\bar{x}$ to find upper range limit:
+ 15.65 =	15.90	$= \bar{x} + \dfrac{s_x}{\sqrt{n}} \, t$
15.65 − RCL 0 =	15.40	$= \bar{x} - \dfrac{s_x}{\sqrt{n}} \, t$

Decision time:

15.50 oz amount of red tint specified

15.40   15.90

From the small sample of 8 cans it can be stated, with 90% certainty, that the population mean value for the red tint is between 15.4 and 15.9 oz. Since the specified value of 15.5 lies between these limits, the process appears to be acceptable.

PHARMACEUTICAL SPECIFICATIONS

Pharmaceutical Specifications

This example involves testing a claim using data from a small sample with concern about the maximum specification only.

You are called in to help the buyer for a large chain of drugstores. A large shipment of cough medicine has arrived. The manufacturer claims that the preparation contains 8% alcohol. The buyer needs to be certain that the population's mean alcohol content is no greater than 8%. He can only get data on a small sample: 5 bottles were selected at random and analyzed. The bottles showed 7.85%, 8.33%, 7.97%, 8.31% and 7.76% alcohol upon test. Should you advise the buyer to reject the shipment? He says he would like to be 95% sure of his decision.

 Target: In this case you need to find out all you can about the population mean (μ) from the small sample. The concern is that the mean alcohol content of the shipment is not over 8%.

Tools: You are dealing with a small sample (n<30), so use the statistical analysis method suitable for small sample analysis. First enter the sample data with the $\boxed{\Sigma +}$ key, and calculate the sample mean ($\bar{x}$) and sample standard deviation (s_x) with the $\boxed{2nd}$ $\boxed{\text{Mean}}$ and $\boxed{2nd}$ $\boxed{\text{On-1}}$ keys. Next, using the formula below, calculate the predicted range for the population mean:

Predicted range for
the population mean $= \bar{x} \pm \dfrac{s_x}{\sqrt{n}}\, t$

In this formula
$\quad \bar{x}$ is the sample mean,
$\quad s_x$ is the sample standard deviation,
$\quad n$ is the number of items in the sample (5), and
$\quad t$ is the "t" value found in the Appendix.

The t value is found in Table B, because you are concerned with only one limit. Locate the t value for the degree of certainty required (95%) and the number of degrees of freedom (df) equal to $(n - 1) = 4$. The t value is 2.132.

PHARMACEUTICAL SPECIFICATIONS

Keying it in: Enter the data using the $\boxed{\Sigma+}$ key, and calculate the sample mean and standard deviation values:

Press	Display	Comments
$\boxed{ON/C}$ $\boxed{ON/C}$ $\boxed{2nd}$ $\boxed{CSR}$	0.00	Clear display, pending operations, and statistical registers
7.85 $\boxed{\Sigma+}$	1.00	Enter the data: the calculator
8.33 $\boxed{\Sigma+}$	2.00	keeps count of the number
7.97 $\boxed{\Sigma+}$	3.00	of entered data points
8.31 $\boxed{\Sigma+}$	4.00	
7.76 $\boxed{\Sigma+}$	5.00	
$\boxed{2nd}$ $\boxed{Mean}$	8.04	The sample mean ($\bar{x}$)
$\boxed{2nd}$ $\boxed{σn-1}$	0.26	The sample standard deviation (s_x)

Clear the calculator and calculate the predicted range for the population mean.

First calculate $\dfrac{s_x}{\sqrt{n}}$ t and store it,

then calculate $\bar{x} \pm \dfrac{s_x}{\sqrt{n}}$ t.

Press	Display	Comments
$\boxed{ON/C}$ $\boxed{ON/C}$	0.00	Clear display and pending operations
$\boxed{2nd}$ $\boxed{Fix}$ 2	0.00	Fix decimal to two places
.26 $\boxed{\div}$ 5 $\boxed{\sqrt{x}}$ $\boxed{X}$ 2.132	2.132	
$\boxed{=}$ $\boxed{STO}$ 0	0.25	Now add x to calculate $\bar{x} + \dfrac{s_x}{\sqrt{n}}$ t.
$\boxed{+}$ 8.04 $\boxed{=}$	8.29	Upper limit Now calculate $\bar{x} - \dfrac{s_x}{\sqrt{n}}$ t.
8.04 $\boxed{-}$ $\boxed{RCL}$ 0 $\boxed{=}$	7.79	Lower limit

Decision time:

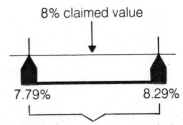

8% claimed value

7.79%   8.29%

Predicted range of the population
mean based on the small sample.

Based on the small number of samples, the actual amount of alcohol may be as low as 7.79%. Since the claimed value is 8%, you
can accept the shipment. In this case the entire predicted range of
the population mean would have to be greater than 8% before re-
jecting the shipment with 95% certainty.

Defective Parts

This example involves checking on a proportion of defective parts with concern about the maximum percentage defective only.

You are called in to aid a flashlight manufacturer. He has just received his first shipment of flashlight bulbs from a new supplier and wants to be particularly sure the shipment is good before accepting it. Testing the parts is quite simple in this case (they either light or they do not), so a sizeable sample can be easily tested. The new bulb supplier insists that the shipment (population) will contain no more than 12% defective bulbs.

The line foreman has 250 of the bulbs tested, and of these, 43 (17.2%) fail. He asks your advice: Should the shipment be accepted or rejected based on this data? He would like to be 90% sure the lot has more than 12% defective bulbs, before he rejects the shipment and looks for a new vendor.

Target: This example deals with a claim about a proportion, so you should use a statistical technique especially suited to handling the problem. First, use the formula below to calculate the predicted range of the population mean, as in previous examples. In this case, however, instead of the population mean being a numerical value (such as weight, or percent volume) it is the proportion of defective parts in the population.

The formula for the range is:

Predicted range of the

$$\text{population mean proportion} = \bar{P} \pm \left(\frac{\bar{P}(1 - \bar{P})}{n} \right)^{1/2} z.$$

where: $\bar{P}$ is the proportion of defective parts found in the sample (In this case $\frac{43}{250}$ or 0.172);

n is the sample size (250);
   and,
z is the z value found from Table A in the Appendix.

Only one limit is of concern; you should reject if the shipment is over 12% defective, and accept otherwise. Since you wish to be 90% sure of a decision to reject, the z value from Table A is found from column 1 to be 1.28.

Keying it in: The proportion of defective parts in the sample is 17.2% or 0.172. Evaluate the expressions

$$\bar{P} + \left(\frac{\bar{P}(1 - \bar{P})}{n}\right)^{1/2} z \text{ and } \bar{P} - \left(\frac{\bar{P}(1 - \bar{P})}{n}\right)^{1/2} z$$

to calculate the predicted range of the mean.

Begin by evaluating $\left(\frac{\bar{P}(1 - \bar{P})}{n}\right)^{1/2}$, and storing it.

Later in this section, this expression is solved again using a different value for z. Storing the value of $\left(\frac{\bar{P}(1 - \bar{P})}{n}\right)^{1/2}$ in a data memory allows for a much quicker evaluation.

Press	Display	Comments
[ON/C] [ON/C] [2nd] [Fix] 3	0.000	Clear display and pending operations and fix decimal to show three places
.172 [X] [(] 1 [−] .172 [)]	0.828	$\bar{P}(1 - \bar{P})$
[÷] 250 [=] [√x] [STO] 0	0.024	$\left(\frac{\bar{P}(1 - \bar{P})}{n}\right)^{1/2}$ stored in memory 0
[X] 1.28 [+] .172 [=]	0.203	Upper limit
.172 [−] [(] [RCL] 0	0.024	Recall $\left(\frac{\bar{P}(1 - \bar{P})}{n}\right)^{1/2}$ from memory 0
[X] 1.28 [=]	0.141	Lower limit

Decision time:

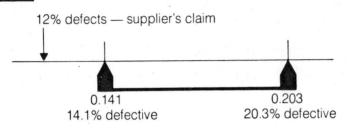

12% defects — supplier's claim

0.141
14.1% defective

0.203
20.3% defective

Predicted range for the mean percentage of
defective parts in the population.

In this case the lowest expected percentage of defective parts is
14.1%. You are 90% sure that the supplier is not meeting his claim
and the manufacturer's needs. Based on this analysis, you advise
the foreman to reject the shipment.

Going further: The foreman is not immediately ready to return the
bulbs. He needs to be very sure. (The president of the supplier is
also the son-in-law of the manufacturer.) You can recheck the decision at a higher degree of certainty quite easily. Suppose
you both agree that if he is 95% sure the shipment is
bad it will go back. First locate the z score in table A for
a 95% degree of certainty. Then recalling the value in
memory 0 calculate the new limits.

Press	Display	Comments
ON/C ON/C	0.000	Clear display and pending operations
.172 + (RCL 0	0.024	
X 1.65 =	0.211	New upper limit
.172 − (RCL 0	0.024	
X 1.65 =	0.133	New lower limit

At 95% certainty, you would still reject the shipment.

Note that increasing the degree of certainty that the shipment contains more than 12% defective bulbs also increases the probability
of not detecting whether there are more than 12% defective bulbs.

Testing for Change

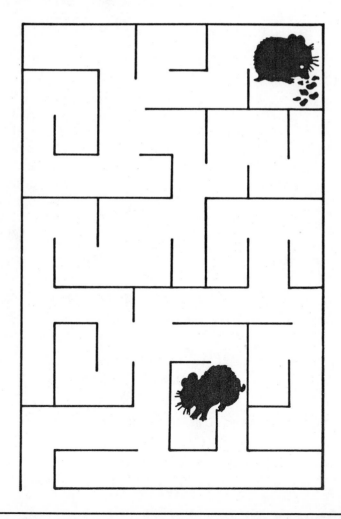

Introduction

In a variety of situations, decisions must be made concerning whether some new process or method has created a significant change when compared to an old one. Situations such as this may arise when trying new educational techniques, production methods, or engineering systems.

Sometimes the results of a change may appear to be obvious. In other cases, however, it may appear that some improvement has been made, but it is not clear that the change is enough to justify the problems that always accompany such changes. Decision-making becomes more difficult in such a situation, and a decision to endorse or institute a new procedure or process, based on data from small samples, can be difficult.

Several statistical methods are available to aid in the study of change. These methods involve some fairly sophisticated techniques, which are presented as a series of step-by-step procedures.

The statistical method being illustrated in this chapter is called a confidence interval procedure. It often is used with another procedure called the "F-test." These two procedures enable you to decide, to a selected degree of certainty, whether a significant difference exists between one set of data and another (assuming that the populations are approximately normal).

This chapter uses the F-test and confidence interval methods to analyze two case histories in order to determine whether a change or difference exists between the results of two processes.

Coated vs. Bare Pipe

This case history uses paired observations with an uncorrected "confidence interval" method for analyzing change.

A new pipe supplier claims that its coating process provides "up to three times longer life" over standard, uncoated pipe. The decision to change to a new pipe will involve a significant unit cost increase, and a pipeline several hundred miles long is to be built, so you need to be 95% certain about the decision.

The data which supports the claim is based on the results of six experiments. In each experiment a length of standard pipe and a length of coated pipe were buried side by side, in six different locations, and the weight loss due to corrosion was measured in ounces per foot per year. The results of the tests are tabulated below:

TEST DATA
(yearly weight loss in ounces/foot/year)

Uncoated Steel Pipe	Coated Pipe
3.68	2.68
1.28	0.45
1.84	0.92
3.68	1.69
1.83	0.05
6.00	0.16

Target: Determine how much better the pipe actually is. Since the sample (6 coated and 6 uncoated pipes) is small, methods of "statistical inference" are important here. You need to predict what the mean difference in yearly weight loss would be between a coated and an uncoated pipeline, based on the experimental data (the sample) at a 95 percent degree of certainty.

Tools: First, examine the mean and standard deviation values for the pipe weight loss. Then, using the methods of statistical inference, determine the range of difference in weight loss between pipelines built of coated and uncoated pipe.

This type of data is called paired observations because each coated pipe has been paired with one uncoated pipe. By considering the difference within each pair, any differences in soils, climates, or other variables between the pairs are removed. The first step is to calculate the mean and standard deviation of the paired differences.

Keying it in: First calculate the difference between the coated and uncoated weight loss in each pair, being careful not to reverse the order of the numbers in each pair. Then find the mean and standard deviation.

If necessary, clear the statistical registers with [2nd] **CSR** .

Press	Display	Comments
[ON/c] [ON/c] [2nd] **Fix** 4	0.0000	Clear display and pending operations and fix decimal at 4 places
3.68 [−] 2.68 [=] [Σ+]	1.0000	Enter data for differences
1.28 [−] .45 [=] [Σ+]	2.0000	between coated and
1.84 [−] .92 [=] [Σ+]	3.0000	uncoated pipe
3.68 [−] 1.69 [=] [Σ+]	4.0000	
1.83 [−] .05 [=] [Σ+]	5.0000	
6 [−] .16 [=] [Σ+]	6.0000	
[2nd] **Mean**	2.0600	Mean weight loss for differences
[2nd] **σn-1**	1.9135	Standard deviation

Now use the confidence interval procedure to determine the range of difference in mean weight loss between the uncoated and coated pipe. First find the t value for the degree of surety needed (here 95%) where the degrees of freedom are $(n − 1) = 5$, since we have six paired observations. Use Table B in the Appendix

because only the improvement of uncoated over coated pipe is of interest. The t value is 2.015. Now calculate the range of predicted differences for the means with the same formula used in the pharmaceutical example in Chapter 7.

$$\text{Predicted range for the population mean} = \bar{x} \pm \frac{s_x}{\sqrt{n}} \, t$$

In this case:

$$\bar{x} = 2.06;$$
$$n = 6;$$
$$s_x = 1.9135;$$
$$\text{and,}$$
$$t = 2.015.$$

Press	Display	Comments
[ON/c] [ON/c]	0.0000	Clear display and pending operations
1.9135 [÷] 6 [√x] [X]	0.7812	Determine the value to be
2.015 [=] [STO] 0	1.5741	added and subtracted
[+] 2.06 [=]	3.6341	The upper limit
2.06 [−] [RCL] 0 [=]	0.4859	The lower limit

Decision time: Based on this analysis of the data, there is a 95% confidence that the difference in the means between a coated and an uncoated pipeline is between 3.6314 and 0.4859 ounces per foot per year. This means that, with 95% certainty, the coated pipe will perform better than the uncoated pipe by as much as 3.6314 ounces per foot per year or by as little as 0.4859 ounces per foot

per year or any value in between. This is all that can be concluded based on only six experiments. The claim of "up to three times" better performance seems to be accurate, but it could also be "as little as a few percent better performance."

With this information, consider other factors involved in changing to the new pipe, such as what extra costs are involved in changing to the coated pipe, how long the pipeline needs to last, the specific soil in which the pipe will be laid, and the other factors surrounding the decision. The analysis of this data puts you in a better bargaining position with the supplier. It also shows how much (or how little) information can be drawn from a small amount of data.

Biological Data

This example uses a corrected confidence interval method for analyzing change.

A biology student needs help in analyzing data he has taken from an experiment. He is testing to see whether a certain drug has any effect on the intelligence level of hamsters, as measured by the time it takes the hamsters to complete a simple maze test. Nine hamsters were fed the drug and given the test, while a control group of 13, which were not treated, were given the same test. The student has tabulated the data for the two groups of hamsters:

	No Drug	Treated with Drug
number of hamsters in sample	13	9
mean time to complete maze	110.01	101.58
standard deviation	9.9116	2.8566
square of standard deviation	98.24	8.16

The student's instructor maintains that there is no significant difference between the two groups. The student, however, believes that the drug did create a change, and would like to prove this with a confidence of 99%.

Target: Discover what you can conclude about the performance of the drug based on a small series of tests. Statistical inference enables you to calculate, at a selected certainty level, a confidence interval (range) concerning the difference in intelligence between hamsters treated with the drug and those not treated with the drug. The method used to calculate this range is a two part process. First, an F-test is used. Then, based on the results of this test, a "corrected" or an "uncorrected" confidence interval is calculated.

Tools: To perform the F-test, identify the data with the greatest standard deviation as the "high" data, and data with the lowest value standard deviation as the "low" data. The subscripts "H" and "L" are used to differentiate these two groups. The data, with the necessary labels, are shown below:

	No Drug	Treated with Drug
number of hamsters	$13 = n_H$	$9 = n_L$
mean time to maze test (sec)	$110.01 = \bar{x}_H$	$101.58 = \bar{x}_L$
standard deviation	$9.9116 = Sx_H$	$2.8566 = Sx_L$
square of standard deviation	$98.24 = Sx_H{}^2$	$8.16 = Sx_L{}^2$

To conduct the F-test, calculate the value of $\dfrac{Sx_H{}^2}{Sx_L{}^2}$, and compare the result to the F value found in Table E in the Appendix. (The appropriate F value in this problem is $(n_H - 1) = 12$ degrees of freedom for the numerator, $(n_L - 1) = 8$ degrees of freedom for the denominator, and a 99% degree of certainty.) This gives a value of $F = 5.67$. If the calculated value is less than this value from the table, the F-test is "passed" and you can immediately calculate the confidence interval. If, however, the calculated value is greater than the F value, a corrected confidence interval procedure must be used. The F-test used here is called a "one tailed" test, testing if $Sx_H{}^2$ is greater than $Sx_L{}^2$.

Keying it in: Begin by calculating $\dfrac{Sx_H{}^2}{Sx_L{}^2}$

Press	Display	Comments
⌨ON/c ⌨ON/c ⌨2nd ⌨Fix 3	0.000	Clear display and pending operations and fix display at 3 decimal places
98.24 ➗ 8.16 ✖=	12.039	Value of $\dfrac{Sx_H{}^2}{Sx_L{}^2}$

Since this value is greater than the value found in the F table (5.67), the F-test is not passed, so a corrected confidence interval procedure must be used for the rest of the problem.

The correction to the confidence interval procedure provides a corrected number of degrees of freedom for the problem. Once the corrected number of degrees of freedom is calculated, the appropriate t value is used to calculate the predicted range of difference in the population means.

The corrected number of degrees of freedom is given by the formula:

$$\text{corrected degrees of freedom} = \frac{1}{\left[\dfrac{K^2}{(n_H - 1)} + \dfrac{(1 - K)^2}{(n_L - 1)}\right]}, \quad \text{where } K = \frac{\dfrac{Sx_H^2}{n_H}}{\left(\dfrac{Sx_H^2}{n_H} + \dfrac{Sx_L^2}{n_L}\right)}$$

First evaluate K:

Press	Display	Comments
ON/c ON/c	0.000	Clear display and pending operations
98.24 ÷ 13 =	7.557	
STO 0 ÷	7.557	Value of $\dfrac{Sx_H^2}{n_H}$
(RCL 0 + 8.16	8.16	
÷ 9)	8.464	Value of denominator
= STO 1	0.893	Value of K stored in memory 1

Now calculate the "corrected" number of degrees of freedom:

Press	Display	Comments
1 ÷	1.000	
(RCL 1 x^2		
÷ (	0.797	
13 − 1) +	0.066	
(1 − RCL 1)	0.107	
x^2 ÷	0.011	
(9 − 1)) =	14.734	The corrected number of degrees of freedom

Since the F-test was not passed, the range of difference between the two means is calculated using the formula:

$$(\bar{x}_H - \bar{x}_L) \pm \left[\frac{Sx_H{}^2}{n_H} + \frac{Sx_L{}^2}{n_L} \right]^{\frac{1}{2}} t$$

In this case

$\bar{x}_H = 110.01$	$\bar{x}_L = 101.58$
$n_H = 13$	$n_L = 9$
$Sx_H{}^2 = 98.24$	$Sx_L{}^2 = 8.16$

Table C only lists t values for integer values of degrees of freedom (14, 15, etc.). Using the calculator, find the appropriate value of t for 14.734 degrees of freedom using a process called interpolation.

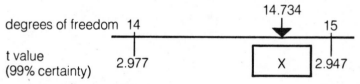

Between degrees of freedom 14 and 15, the t values go from 2.977 to 2.947. The t value for 14.734 degrees of freedom is equal to

$$2.977 - [(14.734 - 14)(2.977 - 2.947)]$$

Press	Display	Comments
ON/c ON/c	0.000	Clear display and pending operations
2.977 − ((14.734 − 14	2.977	Value of t at 14
) ×	0.734	"Distance" from 14 to 14.734
(2.977 − 2.947)	0.030	"Distance" in t values from 14 to 15
) =	2.955	t value for 14.734

With this t value, calculate the range of difference between means using the formula given previously.

Press	Display	Comments
ON/c ON/c	0.000	Clear display and pending operations
110.01 − 101.58 =		
STO 0	8.430	The value of $\bar{x}_H - \bar{x}_L$ stored in memory 0
98.24 ÷ 13 +	7.557	Next calculate the
8.16 ÷ 9 = √x	2.909	righthand term in the
× 2.955 = STO 1	8.597	equation
	Now add $(\bar{x}_H + \bar{x}_L)$	
+ RCL 0 =	17.027	Upper limit for difference between means
	Subtract second term from first:	
RCL 0 − RCL 1 =	−0.167	Lower limit for difference between means

Decision time: Based on the data, you can state with 99% certainty that the difference between the means lies between 17.027 and −0.167. If the drug had no effect on the hamsters' performance, the difference between the means would be expected to be zero. Since the range of predicted values of the difference between means includes the value zero, you cannot be sure (at a

99% degree of certainty) that a change occurs when the hamsters are treated with the drug. Consequently, there is no statistically significant difference between the two groups at the 99% confidence level. Additional data might be needed to substantiate this finding.

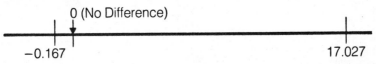

0 (No Difference)

−0.167   17.027

Going further: Would this analysis predict a significant difference between the two groups at the 95% confidence level?

Answer: Yes.

Statistical Theory

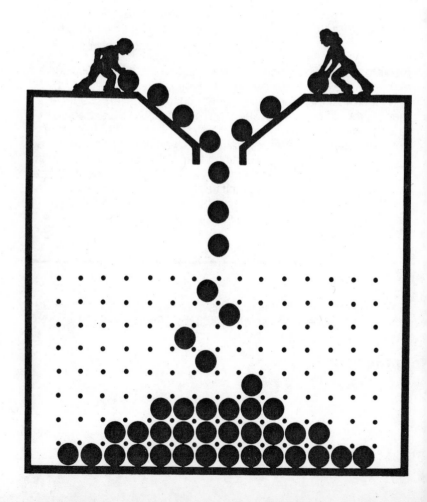

As mentioned in the introduction, the primary focus of this book is how to use statistical tools that are applicable in a variety of business, scientific, and everyday life situations. These techniques can be valuable (and even enjoyable) in bringing more accuracy into decision making with your calculator.

Understanding the why and how of these processes would involve an extended statistics course. Some sources for further reading are suggested in the Bibliography. The following is a quick survey of the key elements of the statistics used in this book.

Small Population

To see a simple example of the theory, start with an analysis of a small body of data that can be handled completely. Consider the test scores for 5 people on a simple exam (statisticians would say that this population consisted of 5 elements). Out of a perfect score of 10, the scores for the students are 4, 5, 6, 7, and 8. The calculator can quickly and easily calculate the *population mean* (labeled μ) and the *population standard deviation* (labeled σ).

Press	Display	Comments
ON/c ON/c 2nd CSR	0	Clear display, pending operations and statistical registers
2nd Fix 2	0.00	Set display to 2 decimal places
4 Σ+	1.00	
5 Σ+	2.00	Calculator keeps a count
6 Σ+	3.00	of the data entries.
7 Σ+	4.00	
8 Σ+	5.00	
	Find the population mean (μ)	
2nd Mean	6.00	
	Find the population standard deviation (σ)	
2nd σn	1.41	

With this small population, all the data can be easily and directly analyzed as illustrated below.

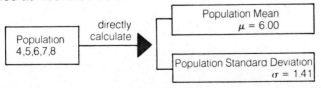

Population 4,5,6,7,8 → directly calculate → Population Mean μ = 6.00 / Population Standard Deviation σ = 1.41

Large Population

Often the population is made up of thousands (or even millions) of items. Even with the calculator helping, entering all that data may be very difficult. In addition, sometimes the measurement may destroy the item. For example, suppose the lifetime of a shipment of batteries is being tested. To test a battery requires depleting it. Doing this to the entire population tells exactly what the mean lifetime for the population is, but also destroys the batteries.

One alternative, in situations like this, is to select a smaller number of items from the population — a sample — and test them. This is where the science of statistics comes in. Based on analyzing the smaller sample, which is cheaper, easier, and more practical than testing the population, methods of statistical inference can be used to make statements about the population mean (μ). The first step is to calculate the sample mean ($\bar{x}$) and the sample standard deviation (s_x). Then statistical techniques are used to determine information about the population, as diagrammed below.

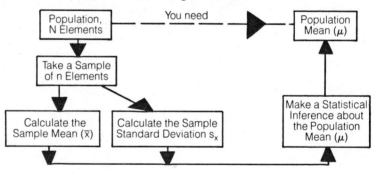

The process of using sample data to determine information about the population contains some chance. The larger the sample, the more likely that your statements about the mean are accurate.

The Sample and the Population

When a small sample is taken from a large population, how representative is it? In the battery example, if the sample contains many batteries with a low lifetime, an entire shipment could be underrated based on their performance. Similarly, if only batteries with a long lifetime are selected, the shipment may be overrated. The following discusses the chances that the sample mean ($\bar{x}$) is near the population mean (μ).

To understand how statisticians study this situation, consider the small population of 5 test scores. Suppose samples of 2 test scores are taken from it and examined. (In practice a population this small would not be handled using statistics, but using it to examine the processes statisticians use demonstrates some important concepts.)

The 5 test scores are 4, 5, 6, 7, 8. The population mean (μ) is 6. What happens if 2 of these scores are selected at random (a sample), and their mean ($\bar{x}$) is determined? What are the chances that the sample mean is also 6, equal to the population mean?

To answer this question, examine all the possible samples of two test scores that can be drawn out of the population of 5, and then note the sample means for each possibility. This is the way statisticians first began looking at the problem of statistical inference. All of the possible samples of 2 test scores are listed in the table below, along with their means.

The method of selection for the test scores at random could be visualized in this way: Put each score on a slip of paper; put the papers into a hat, shake well, pick one out and note it; replace it in the hat; shake again; pick again. The replacement is important. When samples are taken without replacement, a correction factor must be entered into statistical inferences.

Population of 5 Test Scores: 4, 5, 6, 7, 8

The following table lists all possible ways of picking a sample of 2 elements and the mean of each sample.

All Possible Samples of 2 Elements	Value of the Mean for Each Sample	Label for Mean Value
4, 4	4.0	$\bar{X}_1$
4, 5	4.5	$\bar{X}_2$
4, 6	5.0	$\bar{X}_3$
4, 7	5.5	$\bar{X}_4$
4, 8	6.0	$\bar{X}_5$
5, 4	4.5	$\bar{X}_6$
5, 5	5.0	$\bar{X}_7$
5, 6	5.5	$\bar{X}_8$
5, 7	6.0	$\bar{X}_9$
5, 8	6.5	$\bar{X}_{10}$
6, 4	5.0	$\bar{X}_{11}$
6, 5	5.5	$\bar{X}_{12}$
6, 6	6.0	$\bar{X}_{13}$
6, 7	6.5	$\bar{X}_{14}$
6, 8	7.0	$\bar{X}_{15}$
7, 4	5.5	$\bar{X}_{16}$
7, 5	6.0	$\bar{X}_{17}$
7, 6	6.5	$\bar{X}_{18}$
7, 7	7.0	$\bar{X}_{19}$
7, 8	7.5	$\bar{X}_{20}$
8, 4	6.0	$\bar{X}_{21}$
8, 5	6.5	$\bar{X}_{22}$
8, 6	7.0	$\bar{X}_{23}$
8, 7	7.5	$\bar{X}_{24}$
8, 8	8.0	$\bar{X}_{25}$

In a real situation, you would only know *one* of these results. You would have chosen a sample, determined its mean value ($\bar{x}$), and from that result be trying to calculate or deduce the population mean value (μ). Look for a moment at the sample mean values. The population mean is 6. What appear to be the chances of picking an $\bar{x}$ of 6 at random?

POPULATION OF 5 TEST SCORES: 4, 5, 6, 7, 8

The picture below shows how the sample means (the $\bar{x}$'s) vary by putting each mean value in its place.

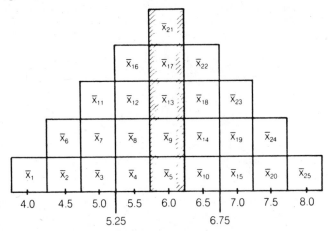

Values for the Sample Means

In this picture there is a mean label inside each little box. The boxes are stacked according to the value of their means. This picture represents the chances, for a sample picked at random, of finding one with a sample mean equal to the population mean value of 6. Five of the sample means ($\bar{x}_{21}$, $\bar{x}_{17}$, $\bar{x}_{13}$, $\bar{x}_9$ and $\bar{x}_5$, in the center boxes) each have mean values of 6. In fact, the most probable choice is a value of 6. For large populations (N over 100) and large samples (n over 30), the general rule is:

The most probable value of $\bar{x}$ is the population mean (μ).

Relative Areas

The relative areas of the boxes illustrate the chances that a sample chosen at random will have a $\bar{x}$ of 6. There are 25 boxes and 5 of them contain 6's, so the chances are the ratio of the shaded boxes to the total area of all the boxes, $\frac{5}{25}$ or 20%.

This picture also shows the chances of obtaining values of $\bar{x}$ that are close to μ. The chances of picking a sample at random whose $\bar{x}$ was 6 ± 0.75 (an x value from 5.25 to 6.75) can be determined by counting the boxes containing $\bar{x}$'s between 5.25 and 6.75, and dividing by the total number of boxes. The chances in this case are $\frac{13}{25}$ or 52%.

Consider what would happen to our picture if the number of elements in the population increased from 5 to 100, and the sample size increased from 2 to 30. Arranging all the sample means pictorially would show something like the behavior shown below.

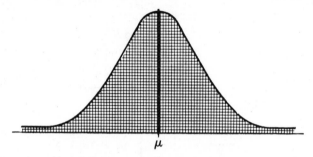

As the boxes get smaller and smaller (they would be very small in this case, for with N=100 and n=30 there are 10^{60} boxes), the outside of the picture smooths out into a classic, symmetric shape called the *Normal Curve*. As a general rule, it is assumed in most situations that the $\bar{x}$'s are distributed normally (follow the normal curve) whenever the population has over 100 elements and the sample size is greater than 30.

The Normal Curve

Much has been written about the normal (or "Bell" or "Gaussian") curve. The important part is the areas under the curve, and how they can be used to obtain information about the population mean from the sample mean. Another key element in the normal curve is the standard deviation of the sample means, labeled $\sigma_{\bar{x}}$.

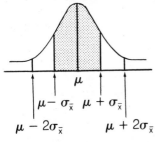

μ

$\mu - \sigma_{\bar{x}}$ $\mu + \sigma_{\bar{x}}$

$\mu - 2\sigma_{\bar{x}}$ $\mu + 2\sigma_{\bar{x}}$

Because the sample means follow this normal behavior (for large populations and samples) some mathematical predictions can be made that apply to almost all situations where large populations and samples are concerned. These results were calculated by statisticians examining areas under the normal curve.

First, examine the normal curve above and note that it is partitioned into 4 sections, each of which is separated by $\sigma_{\bar{x}}$. The shaded area includes all the sample means whose values are between $\mu - \sigma_{\bar{x}}$ and $\mu + \sigma_{\bar{x}}$. The ratio of this area to the total is 68.26%. Whenever a sample is chosen from a population, the chances are 68.26 out of 100 that its sample mean is within $\pm\ \sigma_{\bar{x}}$ of the population mean. Another way of saying this is that you can be 68.26% sure that the population mean lies somewhere in the range of the sample mean plus or minus $\sigma_{\bar{x}}$.

The standard deviation of the sample means ($\sigma_{\bar{x}}$), is fairly easy to calculate from sample data. For samples with larger than 30 elements ($n > 30$), $\sigma_{\bar{x}}$ can be considered equal to $\dfrac{s_x}{\sqrt{n}}$, where s_x is the sample standard deviation.

The sample standard deviation is readily available. It is the number displayed after entering the sample data (with the ⟦Σ+⟧ and ⟦2nd⟧ ⟦Frq⟧ keys), and then pressing ⟦2nd⟧ ⟦σn-1⟧.

Determining the Predicted Range for μ

With the help of the normal curve, a population can be analyzed, based on a sample, in the following way.

First find the sample mean ($\overline{x}$) and sample standard deviation (s_x) by entering the sample data into the calculator with the $\boxed{\Sigma+}$ and $\boxed{2nd}$ $\boxed{Frq}$ keys and then using the $\boxed{2nd}$ $\boxed{Mean}$ and $\boxed{2nd}$ $\boxed{\sigma n\text{-}1}$ keys. Then, with 68.26% certainty, the population mean (μ) lies between

$$\overline{x} + \frac{s_x}{\sqrt{n}} \text{ and } \overline{x} - \frac{s_x}{\sqrt{n}}$$

That is, the sample data can be used to determine a predicted range for the population mean. This range is as close as possible to the population mean, because of the uncertainty in the process of using sample data to draw conclusions about the population. It can only be stated that, to a certain degree of certainty, the population mean lies somewhere in that range.

Analyzing with Large Samples: z Scores

The predicted range for the population mean above gives the limits for the value of μ to one specific degree of certainty: 68.26%. In most applications it is useful to be able to select the degree of certainty desired (or needed) when making any decision about a population based on sample data.

Tables have been constructed based on the areas under different portions of the normal curve. These tables are called tables of "z values" or "z scores", and they enable calculating a predicted range for μ to a selected degree of certainty. (A z value table is included in the Appendix.)

To use the table, decide how sure you need to be that the calculated range includes the population mean. Check in the z table to find the appropriate z score.

Upper/Lower Limits

Two columns are included in the z table. The column used to find the z score depends on the particular decision situation, as shown in the examples in this book. If the decision involves just an upper or lower value for μ, just one limit, use column I. Otherwise, use column II.

To understand why the z values are different for these two situations, consider the normal curve.

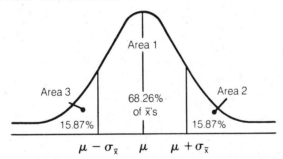

The chance of picking an $\bar{x}$ in area 1 (range $\mu \pm \sigma_{\bar{x}}$) is 68.26%, as discussed earlier. Looking at this another way, the chance of picking an $\bar{x}$ outside of area 1 is $\dfrac{\text{area 2} + \text{area 3}}{\text{total area}}$ or $\dfrac{15.87\% + 15.87\%}{100\%}$

or about $\dfrac{32}{100}$. What is the chance of picking an $\bar{x}$ greater than

$\mu + \sigma_{\bar{x}}$ (checking only an upper limit)? The chance is

$\dfrac{\text{area 2}}{\text{total area}}$ or $\dfrac{15.87\%}{100\%}$ or about $\dfrac{16}{100}$. Since different proportions

of the total area are used, different z scores must be used for these two situations, so two columns are provided in the table.

Procedure for Using z Tables to Calculate the Range for μ

After locating the z score, the predicted range for μ can be calculated using the general formula below.

Predicted range for $\mu = \bar{x} \pm \dfrac{s_x}{\sqrt{n}} z$

where $\bar{x}$ is the sample mean and s_x is the sample standard deviation.

NOTE: For large samples the sample standard deviation (s_x) is nearly equal to the population standard deviation (usually labeled σ). The formula for the range is always correct when written with σ in place of s_x and is quite often written that way in textbooks. z is the z score for the selected degree of certainty.

This particular technique works only for large samples taken from larger populations. (The boundary line for large samples is usually considered 30 elements, and a large population is 100 or more elements.)

Analyzing with Small Samples: t Scores

As the number of samples goes below 30, the normal curve can no longer be accurately used to describe the distribution of the sample means. Statisticians have found a different family of curves that does work (if the population is nearly normally distributed) called t curves.

The shape of any t curve depends on what is called the number of *degrees of freedom* (df) for a particular sample. The number of degrees of freedom in most cases is equal to the number of elements in the sample minus one ($df = n - 1$). The shapes of various t curves are shown in the figure below. Note that for a very large number of degrees of freedom (essentially df = 31 or greater), the t curve becomes the normal curve and z scores can be used.

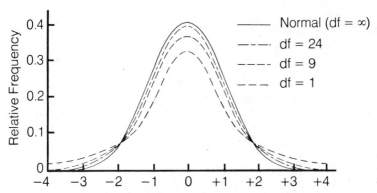

Areas under the t curves have also been tabulated in t score tables in tables B and C in the Appendix. With t scores, small sample data can be analyzed in much the same way as large sample data is analyzed with z scores. Here is the procedure to follow:

With the aid of the calculator, determine the sample mean ($\bar{x}$) and sample standard deviation (s_x).

With this information, you calculate a predicted range for the population mean. Decide how certain you want (or need) to be that the population mean will be in the predicted range. For this level of certainty look up the appropriate t score in Table B or C in the Appendix. (Use Table B if the decision involves only a maximum or minimum value for μ; otherwise use Table C.) The value for df (the degrees of freedom) is the number of elements in the sample minus one ($n - 1$).

After locating the t score, the predicted range for the population mean can be calculated using the formula:

Predicted range for the population mean = $\bar{x} \pm \dfrac{s_x}{\sqrt{n}} \, t$

Summary on Statistical Inference

One process of statistical inference that can be of great use in decision making involves taking data from a sample and from that calculating a predicted range for the population mean. This range shows, to the selected degree of certainty, where the population mean lies. Chapter 7, on testing claims, discusses how to compare this predicted range for the population mean to the mean value claimed by a manufacturer or supplier for a given product, part, etc. If the claimed mean value does not fall in the predicted range, there may be a problem and you may want to reject a shipment or talk further with the supplier. Using data from a sample, you can make more accurate decisions about claims being made for a population using the calculator and statistics.

The steps involved in the process of statistical inference are summarized in the following diagram.

SUMMARY ON STATISTICAL INFERENCE

Steps in Analyzing Sample Data, to Calculate the Predicted Range for the Population Mean:

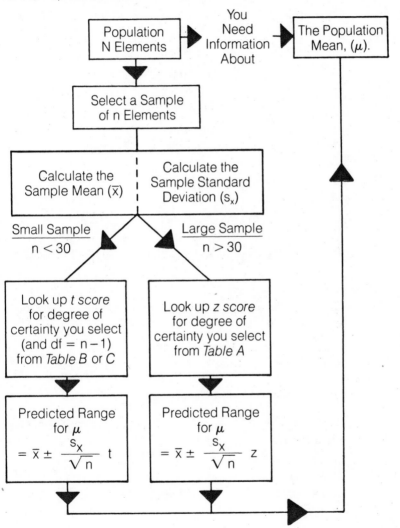

Standard Deviation

To be as accurate as possible, statisticians use two formulas for calculating standard deviation. When calculating the standard deviation of a population (σ) they use the formula:

$$\sigma = \sqrt{\frac{\Sigma_i(x_i - \bar{x})^2}{N}},$$

where N is the number of elements in the population.

NOTE: The symbol Σ_i used here (and elsewhere) means "the sum of". In this case $\Sigma_i(x_i - \bar{x})^2$ means to add all the values of $(x_i - \bar{x})^2$ for i going from 1 to N.

When handling an entire population, enter the data with the $\boxed{\Sigma+}$ and $\boxed{\text{2nd}}$ $\boxed{\text{Frq}}$ keys, and calculate:

— the population mean (μ) by pressing $\boxed{\text{2nd}}$ $\boxed{\text{Mean}}$

— the standard deviation of the population (σ) by pressing $\boxed{\text{2nd}}$ $\boxed{\text{On}}$.

When calculating the standard deviation of a sample, (s_x), the formula used is:

$$s_x = \sqrt{\frac{\Sigma_i(x_i - \bar{x})^2}{n-1}},$$

where n is the number of elements in the sample.

When handling a sample, enter the data with the $\boxed{\Sigma+}$ and $\boxed{\text{2nd}}$ $\boxed{\text{Frq}}$ keys, and calculate:

— the sample mean ($\bar{x}$) by pressing $\boxed{\text{2nd}}$ $\boxed{\text{Mean}}$

— the sample standard deviation (s_x) by pressing $\boxed{\text{2nd}}$ $\boxed{\text{On-1}}$.

The complete reasoning behind the difference in these two calculations is beyond the scope of this book. For values of $n > 30$, the difference between these two calculations becomes very small.

Summary

This chapter has surveyed a large amount of information quite briefly. The other chapters of this book show how to use this information in step-by-step, easy to apply procedures, along with keystroke sequences and sample calculations. Using these powerful methods, with the calculator doing the arithmetic, is quite easy, and does not require studying statistics for years. After seeing these methods actually applied, many of the procedures will become clearer.

The number of symbols used in this book has been kept to a minimum. However, for your reference they are tabulated below. A complete table of all symbols used is also included in the Appendix.

	Population	Sample	Calculator Key Sequence
Number of Elements	N	n	Enter Value of Element, Press $\boxed{\Sigma+}$
Mean	σ	$\bar{x}$	Press $\boxed{\text{2nd}}$ $\boxed{\text{Mean}}$
Standard Deviation	$\sigma = \sqrt{\dfrac{\Sigma(x_i - \bar{x})^2}{N}}$,	$s_x = \sqrt{\dfrac{\Sigma(x_i - \bar{x})^2}{n-1}}$,	σ Press $\boxed{\text{2nd}}$ $\boxed{\sigma n}$ s_x Press $\boxed{\text{2nd}}$ $\boxed{\sigma n\text{-1}}$

$\sigma_{\bar{x}}$ = Standard Deviation of the Sample Means

z = z score for a selected degree of certainty

t = t score for a selected degree of certainty and specific number
of degrees of freedom (df)

Statistical Information

Summary of Symbols

df — degrees of freedom
F — F number from Table D or E
n — number of elements in a sample
N — number of elements in a population
r — correlation coefficient
r_{test} — test correlation coefficient
Sx_H — standard deviation of the "high" sample
Sx_L — standard deviation of the "low" sample
s_x — standard deviation of a sample
$\sigma_{\bar{x}}$ — standard deviation of sample means
σ — standard deviation of a population
t — t number from Table B or C
x_i — the ith element of a sample or population
$\bar{x}$ — sample mean
μ — population mean
z — z number from Table A

Table A

z Scores

Degree of Certainty	Column I For Checking Only an Upper or Lower Level	Column II For Checking Both an Upper and Lower Level
60	0.26	0.84
65	0.39	0.94
70	0.53	1.04
75	0.68	1.15
80	0.84	1.28
85	1.04	1.44
90	1.28	1.65
95	1.65	1.96
99	2.33	2.58

Table B

t Scores
(For Checking Only Upper or Lower Limits)

	Level of Certainty			
Degrees of Freedom (df)	90%	95%	99%	99.5%
1	3.078	6.314	31.821	63.657
2	1.886	2.920	6.965	9.925
3	1.638	2.353	4.541	5.841
4	1.533	2.132	3.747	4.604
5	1.476	2.015	3.365	4.032
6	1.440	1.943	3.143	3.707
7	1.415	1.895	2.998	3.499
8	1.397	1.860	2.896	3.355
9	1.383	1.833	2.821	3.250
10	1.372	1.812	2.764	3.169
11	1.363	1.796	2.718	3.106
12	1.356	1.782	2.681	3.055
13	1.350	1.771	2.650	3.012
14	1.345	1.761	2.624	2.977
15	1.341	1.753	2.602	2.947
16	1.337	1.746	2.583	2.921
17	1.333	1.740	2.567	2.898
18	1.330	1.734	2.552	2.878
19	1.328	1.729	2.539	2.861
20	1.325	1.725	2.528	2.845
21	1.323	1.721	2.518	2.831
22	1.321	1.717	2.508	2.819
23	1.319	1.714	2.500	2.807
24	1.318	1.711	2.492	2.797
25	1.316	1.708	2.485	2.787
26	1.315	1.706	2.479	2.779
27	1.314	1.703	2.473	2.771
28	1.313	1.701	2.467	2.763
29	1.311	1.699	2.462	2.756
30	1.310	1.697	2.457	2.750
40	1.303	1.684	2.423	2.704
60	1.296	1.671	2.390	2.660
120	1.289	1.658	2.358	2.617
∞	1.282	1.645	2.326	2.576

STATISTICAL INFORMATION

Table C

t Scores

(For Checking Both Upper and Lower Limits)

Level of Certainty

	80%	90%	95%	99%	99.9%
1	3.078	6.314	12.706	63.657	636.619
2	1.886	2.920	4.303	9.925	31.598
3	1.638	2.353	3.182	5.841	12.941
4	1.533	2.132	2.776	4.604	8.610
5	1.476	2.015	2.571	4.032	6.859
6	1.440	1.943	2.447	3.707	5.959
7	1.415	1.895	2.365	3.499	5.405
8	1.397	1.860	2.306	3.355	5.041
9	1.383	1.833	2.262	3.250	4.781
10	1.372	1.812	2.228	3.169	4.587
11	1.363	1.796	2.201	3.106	4.437
12	1.356	1.782	2.179	3.055	4.318
13	1.350	1.771	2.160	3.012	4.221
14	1.345	1.761	2.145	2.977	4.140
15	1.341	1.753	2.131	2.947	4.073
16	1.337	1.746	2.120	2.921	4.015
17	1.333	1.740	2.110	2.898	3.965
18	1.330	1.734	2.101	2.878	3.922
19	1.328	1.729	2.093	2.861	3.883
20	1.325	1.725	2.086	2.845	3.850
21	1.323	1.721	2.080	2.831	3.819
22	1.321	1.717	2.074	2.819	3.792
23	1.319	1.714	2.069	2.807	3.767
24	1.318	1.711	2.064	2.797	3.745
25	1.316	1.708	2.060	2.787	3.725
26	1.315	1.706	2.056	2.779	3.707
27	1.314	1.703	2.052	2.771	3.690
28	1.313	1.701	2.048	2.763	3.674
29	1.311	1.699	2.045	2.756	3.659
30	1.310	1.697	2.042	2.750	3.646
40	1.303	1.684	2.021	2.704	3.551
60	1.296	1.671	2.000	2.660	3.460
120	1.289	1.658	1.980	2.617	3.373
∞	1.282	1.645	1.960	2.576	3.291

Degrees of Freedom (df)

Table D   **F Values at 95% Level of Certainty**

Degrees of Freedom of the Numerator →

Degrees of Freedom of the Denominator	1	2	3	4	5	6	7	8	9	10	12	15	20	30	60	120	∞
1	161.4	199.5	215.7	224.6	230.2	234.0	236.8	238.9	240.5	241.9	243.9	245.9	248.0	250.1	252.2	253.3	254.3
2	18.51	19.00	19.16	19.25	19.30	19.33	19.35	19.37	19.38	19.40	19.41	19.43	19.45	19.46	19.48	19.49	19.50
3	10.13	9.55	9.28	9.12	9.01	8.94	8.89	8.85	8.81	8.79	8.74	8.70	8.66	8.62	8.57	8.55	8.53
4	7.71	6.94	6.59	6.39	6.26	6.16	6.09	6.04	6.00	5.96	5.91	5.86	5.80	5.75	5.69	5.66	5.63
5	6.61	5.79	5.41	5.19	5.05	4.95	4.88	4.82	4.77	4.74	4.68	4.62	4.56	4.50	4.43	4.40	4.36
6	5.99	5.14	4.76	4.53	4.39	4.28	4.21	4.15	4.10	4.06	4.00	3.94	3.87	3.81	3.74	3.70	3.67
7	5.59	4.74	4.35	4.12	3.97	3.87	3.79	3.73	3.68	3.64	3.57	3.51	3.44	3.38	3.30	3.27	3.23
8	5.32	4.46	4.07	3.84	3.69	3.58	3.50	3.44	3.39	3.35	3.28	3.22	3.15	3.08	3.01	2.97	2.93
9	5.12	4.26	3.86	3.63	3.48	3.37	3.29	3.23	3.18	3.14	3.07	3.01	2.94	2.86	2.79	2.75	2.71
10	4.96	4.10	3.71	3.48	3.33	3.22	3.14	3.07	3.02	2.98	2.91	2.85	2.77	2.70	2.62	2.58	2.54
11	4.84	3.98	3.59	3.36	3.20	3.09	3.01	2.95	2.90	2.85	2.79	2.72	2.65	2.57	2.49	2.45	2.40
12	4.75	3.89	3.49	3.26	3.11	3.00	2.91	2.85	2.80	2.75	2.69	2.62	2.54	2.47	2.38	2.34	2.30
13	4.67	3.81	3.41	3.18	3.03	2.92	2.83	2.77	2.71	2.67	2.60	2.53	2.46	2.38	2.30	2.25	2.21
14	4.60	3.74	3.34	3.11	2.96	2.85	2.76	2.70	2.65	2.60	2.53	2.46	2.39	2.31	2.22	2.18	2.13
15	4.54	3.68	3.29	3.06	2.90	2.79	2.71	2.64	2.59	2.54	2.48	2.40	2.33	2.25	2.16	2.11	2.07
16	4.49	3.63	3.24	3.01	2.85	2.74	2.66	2.59	2.54	2.49	2.42	2.35	2.28	2.19	2.11	2.06	2.01
17	4.45	3.59	3.20	2.96	2.81	2.70	2.61	2.55	2.49	2.45	2.38	2.31	2.23	2.15	2.06	2.01	1.96
18	4.41	3.55	3.16	2.93	2.77	2.66	2.58	2.51	2.46	2.41	2.34	2.27	2.19	2.11	2.02	1.97	1.92
19	4.38	3.52	3.13	2.90	2.74	2.63	2.54	2.48	2.42	2.38	2.31	2.23	2.16	2.07	1.98	1.93	1.88
20	4.35	3.49	3.10	2.87	2.71	2.60	2.51	2.45	2.39	2.35	2.28	2.20	2.12	2.04	1.95	1.90	1.84
21	4.32	3.47	3.07	2.84	2.68	2.57	2.49	2.42	2.37	2.32	2.25	2.18	2.10	2.01	1.92	1.87	1.81
22	4.30	3.44	3.05	2.82	2.66	2.55	2.46	2.40	2.34	2.30	2.23	2.15	2.07	1.98	1.89	1.84	1.78
23	4.28	3.42	3.03	2.80	2.64	2.53	2.44	2.37	2.32	2.27	2.20	2.13	2.05	1.96	1.86	1.81	1.76
24	4.26	3.40	3.01	2.78	2.62	2.51	2.42	2.36	2.30	2.25	2.18	2.11	2.03	1.94	1.84	1.79	1.73
25	4.24	3.39	2.99	2.76	2.60	2.49	2.40	2.34	2.28	2.24	2.16	2.09	2.01	1.92	1.82	1.77	1.71
26	4.23	3.37	2.98	2.74	2.59	2.47	2.39	2.32	2.27	2.22	2.15	2.07	1.99	1.90	1.80	1.75	1.69
27	4.21	3.35	2.96	2.73	2.57	2.46	2.37	2.31	2.25	2.20	2.13	2.06	1.97	1.88	1.79	1.73	1.67
28	4.20	3.34	2.95	2.71	2.56	2.45	2.36	2.29	2.24	2.19	2.12	2.04	1.96	1.87	1.77	1.71	1.65
29	4.18	3.33	2.93	2.70	2.55	2.43	2.35	2.28	2.22	2.18	2.10	2.03	1.94	1.85	1.75	1.70	1.64
30	4.17	3.32	2.92	2.69	2.53	2.42	2.33	2.27	2.21	2.16	2.09	2.01	1.93	1.84	1.74	1.68	1.62
40	4.08	3.23	2.84	2.61	2.45	2.34	2.25	2.18	2.12	2.08	2.00	1.92	1.84	1.74	1.64	1.58	1.51
60	4.00	3.15	2.76	2.53	2.37	2.25	2.17	2.10	2.04	1.99	1.92	1.84	1.75	1.65	1.53	1.47	1.39
120	3.92	3.07	2.68	2.45	2.29	2.17	2.09	2.02	1.96	1.91	1.83	1.75	1.66	1.55	1.43	1.35	1.25
∞	3.84	3.00	2.60	2.37	2.21	2.10	2.01	1.94	1.88	1.83	1.75	1.67	1.57	1.46	1.32	1.22	1.00

← Degrees of Freedom of the Denominator →

Table E **F Values at 99% Level of Certainty**

Degrees of Freedom of the Numerator →

Denom. df	1	2	3	4	5	6	7	8	9	10	12	15	20	30	60	120	∞
1	4052	4999.5	5403	5625	5764	5859	5928	5982	6022	6056	6106	6157	6209	6261	6313	6339	6366
2	98.50	99.00	99.17	99.25	99.30	99.33	99.36	99.37	99.39	99.40	99.42	99.43	99.45	99.47	99.48	99.49	99.50
3	34.12	30.82	29.46	28.71	28.24	27.91	27.67	27.49	27.35	27.23	27.05	26.87	26.69	26.50	26.32	26.22	26.13
4	21.20	18.00	16.69	15.98	15.52	15.21	14.98	14.80	14.66	14.55	14.37	14.20	14.02	13.84	13.65	13.56	13.46
5	16.26	13.27	12.06	11.39	10.97	10.67	10.46	10.29	10.16	10.05	9.89	9.72	9.55	9.38	9.20	9.11	9.02
6	13.75	10.92	9.78	9.15	8.75	8.47	8.26	8.10	7.98	7.87	7.72	7.56	7.40	7.23	7.06	6.97	6.88
7	12.25	9.55	8.45	7.85	7.46	7.19	6.99	6.84	6.72	6.62	6.47	6.31	6.16	5.99	5.82	5.74	5.65
8	11.26	8.65	7.59	7.01	6.63	6.37	6.18	6.03	5.91	5.81	5.67	5.52	5.36	5.20	5.03	4.95	4.86
9	10.56	8.02	6.99	6.42	6.06	5.80	5.61	5.47	5.35	5.26	5.11	4.96	4.81	4.65	4.48	4.40	4.31
10	10.04	7.56	6.55	5.99	5.64	5.39	5.20	5.06	4.94	4.85	4.71	4.56	4.41	4.25	4.08	4.00	3.91
11	9.65	7.21	6.22	5.67	5.32	5.07	4.89	4.74	4.63	4.54	4.40	4.25	4.10	3.94	3.78	3.69	3.60
12	9.33	6.93	5.95	5.41	5.06	4.82	4.64	4.50	4.39	4.30	4.16	4.01	3.86	3.70	3.54	3.45	3.36
13	9.07	6.70	5.74	5.21	4.86	4.62	4.44	4.30	4.19	4.10	3.96	3.82	3.66	3.51	3.34	3.25	3.17
14	8.86	6.51	5.56	5.04	4.69	4.46	4.28	4.14	4.03	3.94	3.80	3.66	3.51	3.35	3.18	3.09	3.00
15	8.68	6.36	5.42	4.89	4.56	4.32	4.14	4.00	3.89	3.80	3.67	3.52	3.37	3.21	3.05	2.96	2.87
16	8.53	6.23	5.29	4.77	4.44	4.20	4.03	3.89	3.78	3.69	3.55	3.41	3.26	3.10	2.93	2.84	2.75
17	8.40	6.11	5.18	4.67	4.34	4.10	3.93	3.79	3.68	3.59	3.46	3.31	3.16	3.00	2.83	2.75	2.65
18	8.29	6.01	5.09	4.58	4.25	4.01	3.84	3.71	3.60	3.51	3.37	3.23	3.08	2.92	2.75	2.66	2.57
19	8.18	5.93	5.01	4.50	4.17	3.94	3.77	3.63	3.52	3.43	3.30	3.15	3.00	2.84	2.67	2.58	2.49
20	8.10	5.85	4.94	4.43	4.10	3.87	3.70	3.56	3.46	3.37	3.23	3.09	2.94	2.78	2.61	2.52	2.42
21	8.02	5.78	4.87	4.37	4.04	3.81	3.64	3.51	3.40	3.31	3.17	3.03	2.88	2.72	2.55	2.46	2.36
22	7.95	5.72	4.82	4.31	3.99	3.76	3.59	3.45	3.35	3.26	3.12	2.98	2.83	2.67	2.50	2.40	2.31
23	7.88	5.66	4.76	4.26	3.94	3.71	3.54	3.41	3.30	3.21	3.07	2.93	2.78	2.62	2.45	2.35	2.26
24	7.82	5.61	4.72	4.22	3.90	3.67	3.50	3.36	3.26	3.17	3.03	2.89	2.74	2.58	2.40	2.31	2.21
25	7.77	5.57	4.68	4.18	3.85	3.63	3.46	3.32	3.22	3.13	2.99	2.85	2.70	2.54	2.36	2.27	2.17
26	7.72	5.53	4.64	4.14	3.82	3.59	3.42	3.29	3.18	3.09	2.96	2.81	2.66	2.50	2.33	2.23	2.13
27	7.68	5.49	4.60	4.11	3.78	3.56	3.39	3.26	3.15	3.06	2.93	2.78	2.63	2.47	2.29	2.20	2.10
28	7.64	5.45	4.57	4.07	3.75	3.53	3.36	3.23	3.12	3.03	2.90	2.75	2.60	2.44	2.26	2.17	2.06
29	7.60	5.42	4.54	4.04	3.73	3.50	3.33	3.20	3.09	3.00	2.87	2.73	2.57	2.41	2.23	2.14	2.03
30	7.56	5.39	4.51	4.02	3.70	3.47	3.30	3.17	3.07	2.98	2.84	2.70	2.55	2.39	2.21	2.11	2.01
40	7.31	5.18	4.31	3.83	3.51	3.29	3.12	2.99	2.89	2.80	2.66	2.52	2.37	2.20	2.02	1.92	1.80
60	7.08	4.98	4.13	3.65	3.34	3.12	2.95	2.82	2.72	2.63	2.50	2.35	2.20	2.03	1.84	1.73	1.60
120	6.85	4.79	3.95	3.48	3.17	2.96	2.79	2.66	2.56	2.47	2.34	2.19	2.03	1.86	1.66	1.53	1.38
∞	6.63	4.61	3.78	3.32	3.02	2.80	2.64	2.51	2.41	2.32	2.18	2.04	1.88	1.70	1.47	1.32	1.00

← Degrees of Freedom of the Denominator

Complex Number Information

Single Variable:

$X = a + bi$

$r = \sqrt{a^2 + b^2}$

$\theta = $ angle in radians $-\pi < \theta \leq \pi$

$\theta = $ signum (b) $\times \cos^{-1}(\frac{a}{r})$, $r \neq 0$

$\quad = \pi/2$, $r = 0$

$X^2 = (a^2 - b^2) + 2abi$

$\sqrt{X} = \sqrt{r}\,(\cos\frac{\theta}{2} + i\sin\frac{\theta}{2})$, θ in radians

$\dfrac{1}{X} = \dfrac{1}{a + bi} = \dfrac{a - bi}{a^2 + b^2}$

$e^X = e^a\cos b + i\,e^a\sin b$

$\ln X = \ln r + i\,\theta$, $X \neq 0$, θ in radians

$\log X = \dfrac{\ln X}{\ln 10}$, $X \neq 0$

$10^X = 10^a + i\ln(10^b)$

Two Variable:

$X = a + bi \quad Y = c + di$

$X + Y = (a + c) + (b + d)\,i$

$X - Y = (a - c) + (b - d)\,i$

$X \times Y = (ac - bd) + (ad + bc)\,i$

$X \div Y = \dfrac{ac + db}{c^2 + d^2} + i\,\dfrac{bc - ad}{c^2 + d^2}$

$Y^X = e^{X\ln Y}$, $Y \neq 0$

$\sqrt[X]{Y} = e^{\frac{\ln Y}{X}}$, $X \neq 0$, $Y \neq 0$

Error Conditions

The display shows "Error" when overflow or underflow occurs or when an improper operation is requested. When this occurs, no entry from the keyboard except [OFF] is accepted until [ON/c] is pressed. Pressing [ON/c] clears the error condition and all pending operations. You must then determine what caused the error and rekey the entry to avoid the problem.

The following list the circumstances which cause "Error" to be displayed. The first section shows the general conditions. Unless otherwise noted they affect all modes. They do not affect statistical data points which have been entered. The errors listed for functions not valid in the complex number mode are not applicable to complex numbers. The second section lists errors due to statistical operations. They clear all data points and reset statistics mode as if [2nd] [CSR] had been pressed. The third section lists errors of the complex number mode.

Section 1—General Error Conditions

1. Number entry or calculation result (including in memories) is outside the range $\pm 1 \times 10^{-99}$ to $\pm 9.9999999 \times 10^{99}$.
2. Multiplying a number greater than 1×10^{99} by another number may cause an error condition.
3. Dividing a number by zero.
4. Calculating [log], [lnx], or [1/x] of zero or calculating the 0th root of any number or zero to the zero power.
5. Calculating [log], [lnx], a power or root of a negative number in normal calculation and statistical modes.
6. Inverse of sine or cosine (arcsine or arccosine) when the absolute value in the display is greater than 1.
7. Tangent of 90° or 270°, $\pi \div 2$ radians or $3\pi \div 2$ radians, 100 grads or 300 grads, or their rotational multiples such as 450°.
8. Having more than 15 open levels of parentheses or more than 4 pending operations.
9. Factorial of any number except a non-negative integer less than 70.
10. Following [RCL], [STO], or [EXC] with an invalid user data memory number (for normal calculation mode n>6, for statistics mode n >1, for complex number mode n>2).
11. When using memory arithmetic, following [STO] with two memory arithmetic operations instead of an operation and a valid user data memory number.

12. When using memory arithmetic, following [RCL] or [EXC] with an operation instead of a valid user data memory number.
13. Calculating the percent change where the second value is equal to zero.
14. Using an argument outside the range given in Accuracy Information for the logarithmic and trigonometric functions.
15. Finding permutations or combinations with more than three digits after the decimal point.
16. Calculating rectangular to polar conversions with values for x and y such that the sum of their squares exceeds the upper or lower limit of the calculator.

Section 2 — Statistical Error Conditions

1. Calculating [On-1] with only one data point.
2. Entering a data point such that $x \leq \pm 1 \times 10^{-50}$ or $x \geq \pm 1 \times 10^{50}$
3. Entering a series of data points such that the sum of their squares exceeds the upper or lower limit of the calculator.
4. Entering more than 99,999 data points.
5. Making it so that there are zero or fewer data points by removing data points with [2nd] [Σ−] or [2nd] [Frq] [2nd] [Σ−].
6. Calculating the slope, intercept, correlation, x', or y' of a line that parallels the y-axis (vertical line).
7. Calculating the correlation or x' of a line that parallels the x-axis (horizontal line).
8. Calculating the slope, intercept, correlation, x', or y', with only one data point entered.

Section 3 — Complex Number Mode Error Conditions

1. Pressing the [K], [(], or [)] keys.
2. Entering real and imaginary parts of a complex number such that the sum of their squares exceeds the upper or lower limit of the calculator.
3. Following [RCL], [STO], or [EXC] with an operation key.
4. Calculating zero to any power or calculating any root of zero in complex number mode.

Accuracy Information

Each calculation produces an 11-digit result which is rounded to an 8-digit standard display. The 5/4 rounding technique used adds 1 to the least significant digit in the display if the next non-displayed digit is five or more. If this digit is less than five, no rounding occurs. In the absence of these extra digits, inaccurate results would frequently be displayed, such as

$$1 \div 3 \times 3 = 0.9999999$$

Because of rounding, the answer is given as 1, but is internally equal to 0.9999999999.

The higher order mathematical functions use iterative calculations. The cumulative error from these calculations in most cases is maintained beyond the 8-digit display so that no inaccuracy is displayed. Most calculations are accurate to ± 1 in the last displayed digit. There are a few instances in the solution of high order functions where display accuracy begins to deteriorate as the function approaches a discontinuous or undefined point. For example, the tangent of 87° is accurate for all displayed digits. However, the tangent of 89.99999° is accurate to only three places. Another example is when the y^x function has a y value that approaches 1 and an x value that is a very large positive or negative number. The displayed result for 1.05^{-160} is accurate for all displayed digits, while 1.0000005^{-16000} is accurate to only five places. In rectangular to polar conversions in all modes, variables more than five orders of magnitude apart display an angle of 0° or 90°.

Trigonometric values can be calculated for angles greater than one revolution. As long as the trigonometric function result is displayed in normal form rather than in scientific or engineering notation, all displayed digits are accurate for any angle from −36,000° to 36,000° and −40,000 to 40,000 grads. The equivalent range in radians ($\pm 200\pi$) is comparable to degrees and grads in accuracy except at rotation multiples of π and $\pi \div 2$. The rounded value of π limits accuracy at these points. In general, the accuracy decreases one digit for each decade outside this range.

D

ACCURACY INFORMATION

The following gives the limits within which the display must be when calculating certain functions.

Function	Limit
$\sin^{-1} x$, $\cos^{-1} x$	$-1 \leq x \leq 1$
$\sinh x$, $\cosh x$	$0 \leq |x| \leq 227.95592$
$\sinh^{-1} x$	$-10^{50} < x < -10^{-50}$, $10^{-50} < x < 10^{50}$, $x = 0$
$\cosh^{-1} x$	$1 \leq x < 10^{50}$
$\tanh^{-1} x$	$-1 < x < 1$
$\ln x$, $\log x$	$1 \times 10^{-99} \leq x < 1 \times 10^{100}$
e^x	$-227.95592 \leq x \leq 230.25850$
10^x	$-99 \leq x < 100$
$x!$	$0 \leq x \leq 69$ where x is an integer

The following gives the range of results of the inverse trigonometric functions.

Arc Function	Range of Resultant Angle
arcsin x	0 to 90°, $\pi \div 2$ radians, or 100G
arcsin −x	0 to −90°, $-\pi \div 2$ radians, or −100G
arccos x	0 to 90°, $\pi \div 2$ radians, or 100G
arccos −x	90° to 180°, $\pi \div 2$ to π radians, or 100G to 200G
arctan x	0 to 90°, $\pi \div 2$ radians, or 100G
arctan −x	0 to −90°, $-\pi \div 2$ radians, or −100G

SERVICE AND WARRANTY INFORMATION

In Case of Difficulty

In the event that you have difficulty with your calculator, the following instructions will help you to analyze the problem. You may be able to correct your calculator problem without returning the unit to a service facility. If the suggested remedies are not successful, contact the Consumer Relations Department by mail or telephone (refer to WARRANTY PERFORMANCE). Please describe in detail the symptoms of your calculator.

Symptom	Solution
Display is blank, shows erroneous results, flashes erratic numbers, or grows dim.	The battery may be discharged. Insert new batteries using the instructions in BATTERY REPLACEMENT.
Display shows erroneous results or error message	Review the operating instructions, including the Error Conditions appendix, to be certain that calculations were performed correctly.

If the above procedure does not correct the difficulty, return the calculator prepaid to the applicable Service Facility listed under Warranty Performance.

Battery Replacement

NOTE: The calculator cannot hold data in its user data memories or mode registers when the batteries are removed or become discharged.

The calculator uses 2 of any of the following batteries for up to 750 hours of operation: Panasonic LR-44, Ray-O-Vac RW-82, Union Carbide (Eveready) A-76, or the equivalent. For up to 2000 hours of operation use Mallory 10L14, Union Carbide (Eveready) 357, Panasonic WL-14, Toshiba G-13, Ray-O-Vac RW-42, or the equivalent.

1. Turn the calculator off. Place a small screwdriver, paper clip, or other similar instrument into the slot and gently lift the battery cover.

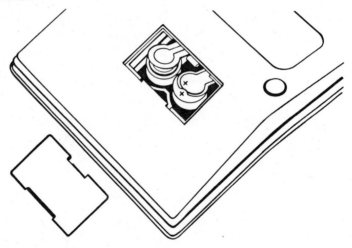

2. Remove the discharged batteries and install new ones as shown. Be careful not to crease the film contacts while installing the new batteries. Be sure the film contacts are positioned to lay on top of the batteries after the batteries are installed.

3. Replace the cover top edge first, then gently press until the bottom of the cover snaps into place.

4. Press [ON/c], [ON/c], [2nd] **CSR**, [INV] [Img], [2nd] **CM**, and [ON/c]. The display then shows 0 and is ready to be used.

CAUTION: Do not incinerate the old batteries.

SERVICE AND WARRANTY INFORMATION

One-Year Limited Warranty

THIS TEXAS INSTRUMENTS ELECTRONIC CALCULATOR WAR-
RANTY EXTENDS TO THE ORIGINAL CONSUMER PURCHASER OF
THE PRODUCT.

WARRANTY DURATION: This calculator is warranted to the original
consumer purchaser for a period of one year from the original purchase date.

WARRANTY COVERAGE: This calculator is warranted against defec-
tive materials or workmanship. **THIS WARRANTY DOES NOT COVER
BATTERIES AND IS VOID IF THE PRODUCT HAS BEEN DAMAGED
BY ACCIDENT, UNREASONABLE USE, NEGLECT, IMPROPER SER-
VICE OR OTHER CAUSE NOT ARISING OUT OF DEFECTS IN MATE-
RIAL OR WORKMANSHIP.**

**WARRANTY DISCLAIMERS: ANY IMPLIED WARRANTIES ARIS-
ING OUT OF THIS SALE, INCLUDING BUT NOT LIMITED TO THE IM-
PLIED WARRANTIES OF MERCHANTABILITY AND FITNESS FOR A
PARTICULAR PURPOSE, ARE LIMITED IN DURATION TO THE
ABOVE ONE YEAR PERIOD. TEXAS INSTRUMENTS SHALL NOT BE
LIABLE FOR LOSS OF USE OF THE CALCULATOR OR OTHER INCI-
DENTAL OR CONSEQUENTIAL COSTS, EXPENSES, OR DAMAGES
INCURRED BY THE CONSUMER OR ANY OTHER USER.** Some states
do not allow the exclusion or limitation of implied warranties or conse-
quential damages, so the above limitations or exclusions may not
apply to you.

LEGAL REMEDIES: This warranty gives you specific legal rights, and
you may also have other rights that vary from state to state.

WARRANTY PERFORMANCE: During the above one year warranty
period your TI calculator will either be repaired or replaced with a reconditioned comparable model (at TI's option) when the product is returned,
postage prepaid, to a Texas Instruments Service Facility listed below. In
the event of replacement with a reconditioned model, the replacement
product will continue the warranty of the original calculator or 6 months,
whichever is longer. Other than the postage requirement, no charge will
be made for such repair, adjustment, and/or replacement.

If the calculator is out of warranty, service rates in effect at the time of return will be charged. Please include information on the difficulty experi-
enced with the calculator as well as return address information including
name, address, city, state, and zip code. The shipment should be
carefully packaged and adequately protected against shock and
rough handling.

Texas Instruments Consumer Service Facilities

U. S. Residents:
Texas Instruments Service Facility
P. O. Box 2500
Lubbock, Texas 79408

Canadian customers only:
Geophysical Services Incorporated
41 Shelley Road
Richmond Hill, Ontario, Canada L4C5G4

NOTE: The P.O. Box number listed for the Lubbock Service Facility is for
United States parcel post shipments only. If you use another carrier, the
street address is:

Texas Instruments Incorporated
2305 University Avenue
Lubbock, TX 79415

CALCULATOR EXCHANGE CENTERS

If your calculator requires service, instead of returning the unit to your dealer or to a service facility for repair, you may elect to exchange the calculator for a factory-rebuilt calculator of the same model (or equivalent model specified by TI) by bringing the calculator in person to one of the exchange centers which have been established across the United States. No charge will be made for the exchange with proof-of-purchase during the first 90 days. The exchanged unit will be in warranty for the remainder of the original warranty period or for 6 months, whichever is longer. A handling fee will be charged for exchange after 90 days from the date of purchase. Out-of-warranty exchanges will be charged at the rates in effect at the time of the exchange. To determine if there is an exchange center in your locality, look for Texas Instruments Incorporated Exchange Center in the white pages of your telephone directory or look under the Calculator and Adding Machine heading in the yellow pages. Please call the exchange center for the availability of your model. Write or call the Consumer Relations Department for further details and the location of the nearest exchange center.

MAILING INSTRUCTIONS

Enclose a written explanation of the problem with your calculator. Be sure to include your name and return address.

Wrap your calculator in tissue or similar soft packing material and enclose it in a strong, crushproof mailing carton. If you use the original display box for mailing, it cannot be returned to you.

To protect your calculator from theft, do not write "calculator" on the outside of the package. Send your calculator to the appropriate address listed in WARRANTY PERFORMANCE.

Texas Instruments strongly recommends that you insure the product for value prior to mailing.

IF YOU NEED SERVICE INFORMATION

If you have questions concerning calculator repair, accessory purchase or the basic functions of your calculator, please call our Consumer Relations Department at (800) 858-1802 (toll free within the contiguous United States except Texas) or (800) 692-1353 (within Texas). If outside the contiguous United States call (806) 741-2646. We regret that we cannot accept collect calls at this number.

SERVICE AND WARRANTY INFORMATION

FOR TECHNICAL ASSISTANCE

For technical questions such as specific calculator applications, etc., you can call (806) 747-3841. We regret that this is not a toll-free number, and we cannot accept collect calls. As an alternative, you can write to:

> Texas Instruments Consumer Relations
> P. O. Box 53
> Lubbock, Texas 79408

California and Oregon: Consumers in California and Oregon may contact the following Texas Instruments offices for additional assistance or information.

Texas Instruments Consumer Service
831 South Douglas Street
El Segundo, California 90245
(213) 973-1803

Texas Instruments
  Consumer Service
6700 Southwest 105th St.
Kristin Square, Suite 110
Beaverton, Oregon 97005
(503) 643-6758

Because of the number of suggestions which come to Texas Instruments from many sources, containing both new and old ideas, Texas Instruments will consider such suggestions only if they are freely given to Texas Instruments. It is the policy of Texas Instruments to refuse to receive any suggestions in confidence. Therefore, if you wish to share your suggestions with Texas Instruments, or if you wish us to review any calculator program key sequence which you have developed, please include the following in your letter:

"All of the information forwarded herewith is presented to Texas Instruments on a nonconfidential, nonobligatory basis; no relationship, confidential or otherwise, expressed or implied, is established with Texas Instruments by this presentation. Texas Instruments may use, copyright, distribute, publish, reproduce, or dispose of the information in any way without compensation to me."

Bibliography

Anthony, Robert N. and Glen A. Welsch. *Fundamentals of Management Accounting.* Homewood, Illinois: Richard D. Irwin, 1974

Anthony, Robert N. and James S. Reece. *Management Accounting Text and Cases.* Fifth edition. Homewood, Illinois: Richard D. Irwin, 1975.

Brooks, David W. and Fred Sicilio. *Chemical Concepts.* Second Edition. Boston: Willard Grant Press, 1971.

Chou, Ya-lun. *Statistical Analysis.* New York: Holt, Rinehart and Winston, 1975.

Churchill, Ruel V. *Complex Variables and Applications.* Second Edition. New York: McGraw-Hill, Inc., 1960.

Ferguson, George A. *Statistical Analysis in Psychology and Education.* New York: McGraw-Hill Book Company, 1966.

Freund, John E. *Mathematical Statistics.* Englewood Cliffs, New Jersey: Prentice-Hall, Inc., 1962.

Grant, Eugene L. and W. Grant Ireson. *Principles of Engineering Economy.* Fifth Edition. New York: The Ronald Press Company, 1970.

Hildebrand, Francis B. *Advanced Calculus for Applications.* Englewood Cliffs, New Jersey: Prentice-Hall, Inc., 1962.

Hummel, Paul M. and Charles Seebeck. *Mathematics of Finance.* New York: McGraw-Hill Book Company, 1971.

Kreyszig, Erwin. *Advanced Engineering Mathematics.* Second Edition. New York: John Wiley and Sons, Inc., 1967.

Nelson, Alfred L., Karl W. Folley, Max Coral. *Differential Equations.* Second Edition. Boston: D.C. Heath and Company, 1960.

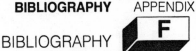

Nichols, Eugene D., Ralph T. Heimer, and E. Henry Garland. *Modern Intermediate Algebra.* New York: Holt, Rinehart and Winston, Inc., 1965.

Oliva, Ralph A., M. Dean LaMont and Linda R. Fowler. *Student Calculator Math Book.* Dallas: Texas Instruments, Inc. 1980.

Schilling, Eugene W. *Electrical Engineering.* Scranton, Pennsylvania: International Textbook Company, 1958.

Washington, Allyn J. *Basic Technical Mathematics.* Second Edition. Menlo Park, California: Cummings Publishing Company, Inc., 1970.

Weston, J. Fred and Eugene F. Brigham: *Essentials of Managerial Finance.* Third Edition. Hinsdale, Illinois: The Dryden Press, 1974.

White, Harvey E. *Introduction to college physics.* New York: Van Nostrand-Reinhold Company, 1969.

Whitsitt, II, Robert E., Kathy A. Kelly, M. Dean LaMont, and Dr. Ralph A. Oliva. *Calculator Decision-Making Sourcebook.* Second Edition. Dallas: Texas Instruments Incorporated, 1981.

Index

The following index should be supplemented by looking at the Key Index inside the front cover.

NOTES

NOTES